Land Birds of America

Land Birds

Photographed by
Eliot Porter, Hal Harrison,
Allan Cruickshank, Helen Cruickshank
and thirty other photographers

Published with the cooperation of
THE AMERICAN MUSEUM OF NATURAL HISTORY

# of America

Robert Cushman Murphy

Lamont Curator of Birds and Chairman of the Department,
The American Museum of Natural History

Dean Amadon

Associate Curator of Birds,
The American Museum of Natural History

McGRAW-HILL BOOK COMPANY, INC.

NEW YORK　•　TORONTO　•　LONDON

Published by The McGraw-Hill Book Company, Inc.

First Edition

Prepared and produced by Chanticleer Press, Inc., New York

Library of Congress Card Number: 53-5191

Contents

Land Birds of America

Introduction

NORTH AMERICA has a long and rich tradition in the field of natural history. In pioneering days, however, only a small part of the population took a keen interest in it. The struggle to subdue a wilderness and build collective security in a New World doubtless left too little leisure for an activity widely regarded as "impractical."

In colonial times, books by the naturalists who had traveled in America were far better appreciated in Europe than on our own side of the Atlantic. But here and there we find in our early history a man of affairs who was also an ardent "natural philosopher." Such was Benjamin Franklin and, equally, Thomas Jefferson. The catalogue of the latter's books at Monticello, his own writings, and his correspondence with scholars here and abroad all reveal an outstanding comprehension of nature and particularly of nature in relation to man. That such taste remained rare in the young Republic is well shown by an entry, made after 1840, in Audubon's journal. Referring to a New England city rich in cultural resources, in which he was seeking subscriptions for his magnificent folio plates, he noted that the community was full of fine people but that they were evidently not interested in birds!

To gain an idea of the vast extent of the change in popular outlook, we have only to remember that general acceptance of the writings of Thoreau came long after his death in 1862. It was late in the nineteenth century before Americans in the mass began the "discovery of the out-of-doors," a process that has continued ever since. Every aspect of natural history has entered into this appreciation, and ornithology—the science of birds—or at any rate "ornithophily," the love of birds—is surely among the most popular.

Paintings of Birds

In bird portraiture our greatest heritage is that of John James Audubon (1785-1851). There were earlier naturalist-painters who worked on the North American continent, but most of them were hardly artists by the standards of either their day or our own. With few exceptions they followed a convention that depicted birds only in rigid profile, and with little attempt to show them in a natural environment. The plates of several of these painters, such as Mark Catesby (1679-1749), author of *The Natural History of Carolina*, are valued today for their historical interest and quaintly decorative quality rather than as intrinsic works of art.

Audubon founded a totally different

school. He tirelessly watched birds in the field and then drew and colored from freshly killed specimens. He was a gifted and indefatigable draftsman but was not solely self-tutored, for he had enjoyed at least brief instruction under the French academician, David. Furthermore, he discarded the restrictions of profile and displayed his birds from all points of view in the postures and setting of freedom. The bulk of the portraits in *The Birds of America* (1827-1838) set a new standard by depicting the subjects engaged in the activities of living creatures instead of merely standing on perches.

Most subsequent painters of birds, in Europe as well as in America, have sought to continue the Audubon style. With varying success they have turned out thousands of portraits in water color or in the muddy medium which in our own day has come to be called "tempera." These pictures have served their purpose in recording the plumages of almost all species and races of birds and in assisting outdoor identification by members of the increasing number of persons who enjoy birds.

Bird portraits of equal worth with those of Audubon are, however, extremely rare among illustrations executed since his time. There are distinguished paintings of birds but most colored pictures in bird books seem merely to be more and more of the same. Unable or unwilling to develop a new and fresh approach, succeeding generations have produced "imitation Audubons," but their creators have lacked the genius and the flair of the master. Whenever we note a forthcoming book advertised as containing reproductions of "the best paintings of

North American birds since Audubon," we may be confident of disappointment. What we usually encounter is something more or less in the Audubon manner, but either wishy-washy or flint-hard in execution, devoid of the bold *décor* that was Audubon's triumph, and lacking the requisite envelopment of figures in the lights and shadows of the open air.

Certain ornithologists may not agree with this estimate of Audubon's preeminence, but we have yet to find an artist who does not. When we turn to such a published collection of great paintings as Thomas Craven's *Treasury of Art Masterpieces*, we find that Audubon is the only painter of birds to be included among the masters. The book reproduces the superb snowy egret standing in a marsh of the Old South. Craven's comment is:

Audubon was an artist and a great one. As a painter of birds, he fixed a standard that has never been seriously contested, his most reverent emulators being no more than taxidermists. It is comforting to know that his pictures are ornithologically accurate, but of more significance that he brought to his birds the imagination of a poet and the hand of an artist trained in the studio of David. He had an eye for dramatic situations, an infallible sense of placement, and an originality of design determined, in each instance, by the individuality and habitat of his subjects.

Birds in Color Photography

This historical sketch indicates why we

believe that color photography can now teach us much more about our birds than a further multiplication of painters' handiwork. The use of color film rests upon approximately half a century of black-and-white technique as applied to depicting wild animals in motion. We need not labor the question as to whether photography is an art or only a fine craft; whatever name we give it, the result is frequently beautiful and always informing.

It is not strictly true that "the camera cannot lie," because the copying of pattern and color on film, and later on paper, is subject to a variety of optical and chemical hazards. Nevertheless, the camera is free from personal bias. Illustrators and taxidermists prefer to draw or mount their birds in pretty poses, with streamlined contours and unruffled plumage showing no trace of either wear or molt. But through field glasses or the lens of a camera we do not always see birds in such guise. On the wing they float with currents of air and remain well-groomed; but in alighting they are frequently wind-tossed or momentarily off balance. They fall into postures that appear unusual or even positively awkward, a fact

Red-backed Shrike: An Ancient Egyptian Tomb Painting

which Audubon, almost alone among bird painters, had the forthrightness to express in his work. The camera is an accurate recorder of all such matters, and to photography we may look for new and incontrovertible evidence regarding the appearance and the ways of living birds.

For such truth a user of this book will find testimony in every color reproduction between its covers. Consider, for instance, the brilliant and expressive eyes in the close-ups of hawks and owls, the flashing nictitating membrane or "third eyelid" which only a fast lens can stop, the blending colors and mobility of an extruded tongue, the superb balance, boldness, and awareness of birds of prey. Take note of the jeweled beads that rim a pheasant's eye, of the natural camouflage of nesting sandpiper and whip-poor-will, the opalescence of a dove's plumage, and the way a road-runner grasps a captured lizard. If you seek color harmonies that a Paris *couturier* might envy, turn to Lewis's woodpecker, the cedar waxwing, or the white-crowned sparrow. How hummingbirds, with wings that vibrate like an insect's, literally "swim" in the thin medium of the atmosphere; how the nests of closely related flycatchers may be told apart; how the cliff swallow lays its adobe walls; what environment the ruby-crowned kinglet favors in its nesting haunts; how many chicks the thrushes rear; what tree-epiphytes the parula warblers choose for their homes in the South and in the North; where the elusive yellow-breasted chat hides its budding family; why the ovenbird is so called—all these and a hundred other questions can be answered by scrutinizing camera likenesses more faithful than any artist's

brush can paint or any taxidermist can reproduce. Supplemental aid is offered by the text, which is condensed but is designed to be both comprehensive and reliable. This book is not intended to serve primarily for the identification of birds in the field, but it does depict several hundred species of land birds through the unimpeachable records of color photographs, and it attempts to furnish summaries of related ornithological knowledge up to the year of publication.

Birds and Man

As a background to the modern significance of ornithology as a branch of biological science, it is interesting to glance toward its half-forgotten beginnings. Both historic and prehistoric records reveal that men have watched and noted and made use of birds from the earliest times. Falconry was a formalized sport in Egypt and China 2000 years before Christ. Sixteen recognizable kinds of birds appear in the hieroglyphics of the Pharaohs. Birdlore is so nearly a universal human tradition that any lack of interest today is likely to be the abnormal product of the shutting out of nature from urban centers. The elimination of bird life from some modern cities is a result of mechanization and may well mean that the environment has become scarcely more desirable for human residents than for birds.

Birds are the most conspicuous members of the animal kingdom. They may not fill a landscape as the bison once did, or obscure the whole sky like an invading horde of locusts, but at most times and places one can readily observe more birds than any

14

other form of wildlife. Birds are also the most widely distributed of all the higher animals. No land is too hot or too cold, too dry or too wet, no sea too remote, to harbor bird life. They live in the darkest rain forests, and at least a few of them in the dryest deserts. Even on the vast Antarctic Continent, more desolate than any other area of the globe, two or three species of birds have been seen short-cutting from coast to coast.

The folklore, pictographs, and legends of all peoples from the cave men on show the ancient intimacy between birds and man. The early literature of nearly every language is full of birds, both factual and mythical. We all remember the roc of Sindbad the Sailor, which could carry off elephants in its talons. This was not a wholly mythical story. No one has ever seen a living roc because it became extinct in Madagascar before that island was settled even by primitive man. But Arab traders acquired its bones and its eggs, the size of watermelons, which had been preserved in ancient mud, and their imaginations did the rest. The principal error was that they thought it a flying bird, whereas actually the roc, or Aepyornis, was a wingless, immensely heavy, somewhat ostrichlike creature, standing twice the height of a man, the largest bird of which we have any knowledge.

Classical Greek is full of birdlore, most of it legendary and not very realistic, although vivid word pictures often leave no doubt as to the identity of the kinds referred to. There were even "ornithologists" in early Greece, in the sense of men whose chief interest lay in birds. Long before Anacreon sang of the swallow, we find the shadowy name of one Dionysius, who built

fairy tales from bird life. He made the female nightingale the singing member of the family, thus starting a convention that was continued in English literature, even though any observant individual might easily learn that the male is the songster. Izaak Walton, the famous author of *The Compleat Angler* (1653), carrying on the Greek tradition, wrote:

But the nightingale, another of my airy creatures, breathes such sweet loud music out of her little instrumental throat, that it might make mankind to think miracles are not ceased. He that at midnight, when the very labourer sleeps securely, should hear, as I have very often, the clear airs, the sweet descants, the natural rising and falling, the doubling and redoubling of her voice, might well be lifted above earth, and say, "Lord, what music hast Thou provided for the saints in heaven, when Thou affordest bad men such music on earth?"

The Greeks even had a sense of humor concerning birds. For example, they gave the name Bradypous, meaning "slow-foot," to the great bustard, one of the swiftest of all running birds! With tongue in cheek they told yarns about such fanciful creatures as the cinnamon bird, the nest of which was supposed to yield the valuable spice. Everybody knows, too, about the Greek phoenix, the bird periodically reborn, it was said, from its own ashes. Its last reported appearance was in the year 139, but the whole idea of the phoenix enjoyed a revival in 1557, when birds of paradise from New Guinea first became known in Europe. The Papuan natives who had prepared the skins of these birds had removed their feet and

15

legs. Our credulous Renaissance ancestors therefore assumed that these exquisite creatures had never had legs and that they spent their lives sailing above the storied Spice Islands—hence the name "birds of paradise."

The ancient Hebrews, who were mainly country folk, were more factual than the Greeks and Orientals. To judge from the Old Testament, the inheritors of the Land of Canaan were extraordinarily good naturalists. We do not need to appraise as science reference to the ravens which brought bread and flesh to Elijah in the morning and evening, but many bird observations in the Bible are much less supernatural. We read of migration in the "hawk that stretcheth her wings toward the South" and of the turtle, the crane, and the swallow that observe the time of their coming. ("Turtle" in older English always meant dove; the word was not applied to the reptile until 1657.)

Hebrew superstition evidently affected attitudes toward nocturnal birds, those more often heard than seen, or those whose habits were for some reason regarded as reprehensible. The owl, the nightjar, and the cuckoo, for example, were held unclean, and therefore not to be eaten. Also deprecated were the eagle, the ossifrage, and the ospray, all of which names are probably incorrect translations of the original Hebrew. The "eagle" in the Old Testament is usually a vulture, possibly the same white "Pharaoh's chicken" still common around garbage dumps in the Levant and North Africa. The ossifrage or bonebreaker, on the other hand, may have been a true eagle—perhaps the species that caused the death of the poet Aeschylus by dropping a tortoise on his bald head. What the ospray was we do not know, but certainly not the fish hawk now called osprey.

We also learn from the Bible that Solomon sent his quinqueremes to Ophir for ivory and apes and peacocks. A few years ago ornithologists would have confidently stated that there were no peacocks in Africa, where Ophir was supposed to lie, but now Dr. James P. Chapin, of the American Museum of Natural History, has discovered in remote parts of the Congo a new species of pheasant that clearly resembles the Asiatic peacock.

Consider a little authentic ornithological science from the Book of Numbers: "And there went forth a wind from the Lord, and brought quails from the sea, and let them fall by the camp, as it were a day's journey on this side, and as it were a day's journey on the other side . . . and as it were two cubits high upon the face of the earth." These were Old World quails on migration. As a result of shooting and netting in modern times, and the reduction of their breeding areas, they have been sadly reduced in numbers, and yet on occasion they still fall to earth as described by Moses. A recent observer on the desolate Sinai Peninsula, Colonel Richard Meinertzhagen, tells of migrating quails descending and covering the ground until there was no more room for a bird unless it alighted upon the backs of others.

Finally, there are such penetrating observations as the following from the Book of Job:

Gavest thou the goodly wings unto
    the peacocks?
Or wings and feathers unto the ostrich

Which leaveth her eggs on the earth,
And warmeth them in the dust,
And forgetteth that the foot may crush
    them,
Or that the wild beast may trample them.
She is hardened against her young ones,
    as though they were not hers:
Her labour is in vain without fear;
Because God hath deprived her of
    wisdom,
Neither hath he imparted to her
    understanding.
What time she lifteth up herself on high,
She scorneth the horse and his rider.

Few readers of the Bible realize how exact is this passage. Most ornithologists doubtless suppose that we learned only recently that several hen ostriches lay their eggs in a common nest and give little attention to their young because the male is mainly responsible for incubation and parental care. The writer of the Book of Job evidently knew also that birds are not highly intelligent, relying much more upon instinctive behavior than do mammals. Small wonder that Job asks, "Who teacheth us more than the beasts of the earth?"

Bird Names

Land birds are more likely than sea birds to possess local or geographically distinctive names. Most sea fowl belong to the coasts of two or more continents, whereas the great bulk of North American land birds are of different species, and many are of different families, from those of Europe to the east and Asia to the west. When British pioneers settled our Atlantic seaboard, they natu-

American Turkeys: A Sixteenth-century French Woodcut

rally applied traditional English names to birds that were substantially the same as those they had known in their homeland. Thus a raven remained a raven and an eagle an eagle. But many old names were misapplied. Our "goldfinch," for example, is quite unlike the original goldfinch of Britain. "Buzzard," the English name of a hawk, became the name of two kinds of vultures in the Virginia and Carolina colonies. " Jackdaw" was applied to the boat-tailed grackle, a member of a family not found in Europe; "partridge" was tacked on an American quail; and "robin" on a very different bird from its British namesake.

Because the bird fauna of temperate North America proved to be much richer in species than that of western Europe, a host of new names had to be found. Blackbirds, wood warblers, vireos, tanagers, tyrant flycatchers, hummingbirds, and many other families originated, we believe, in the American tropics, but gradually spread northward and became important elements in the bird life of our entire continent. Such families are completely absent in Europe.

To understand the origin of the bird names we use, it is necessary to go back far beyond the settlement, or even the discovery, of America. English is a notably receptive tongue, and we have drawn our bird vocabulary from twenty-five or more languages, ranging from classical Greek and Latin to the tongues of primitive peoples everywhere. In a recent study, Martin Grant, an American ornithologist with a taste for linguistics, calculated that nearly one-quarter of 446 English names of birds have come from other languages. The remaining names, in a descending order of frequency, stem from the bird's call or song, its structure, color, habitat, behavior, food, or a geographical locality. A few take their names from those of human beings (*e.g.*, Lucy's warbler), a few from allegedly human characteristics (mostly uncomplimentary, such as booby and dodo), and the source of some is utterly lost in antiquity.

A vernacular name is, by definition, one that comes from everyday speech. "Goatsucker," for example, is a translation of a term in use among Roman countrymen more than two thousand years before technical names of birds were thought of. "Thrush" and "swallow" are old English names derived from antecedent Teutonic. "Meadowlark" is genuine North American vernacular; the bird is not a lark, but it *is* a meadowlark, and any attempt to fit honest common names for plants and animals into the Procrustean bed of scientific classification is properly doomed to fail. Vernacular names are more significant (and have thus far proved more durable and consistent) than technical names.

From the evolution of English names we can learn much about the relationship between certain birds and our forebears. In the fourteenth century, the wren, redbreast, titmouse, pie, and daw were among the birds most familiar around the rural homes of the British. Soon these birds, whether because of endearing qualities or mischievousness, began to be given first names. By the sixteenth or the early seventeenth century, the pie had become Mag, the daw Jack, and the wren Jenny. The redbreast had apparently been dubbed Robin at an even earlier date, because the latter name alone, without redbreast, appeared in print in 1549. By 1709 the blue titmouse had become Tom. In 1713 Jonathan Swift commented on the trend:

Pyes and daws are often stil'd
With Christian nick-names like a child.

Jenny wren proved to be only a loose, though still recognizable, association, but tomtit was welded to stay. Jackdaw and magpie each grew so thoroughly into single words that few persons remember that the birds ever had one-syllable names. And the round, fluffy, big-eyed redbreast, which sits and declaims confidently on the very window sills of British dwellings, stole so completely into the hearts of the people that in time its original name was forgotten and it became known by its baptismal name of Robin. The English colonists who settled here brought the name with them and bestowed it upon the much larger American red-breasted thrush, which occupied a similar niche in their daily lives, as it still does in ours.

Some birds have several or many names. These may be, so to speak, a matter of geography. Our British cousins, having the "real robin" themselves, insist upon calling our robin the "American migratory thrush." But the Australians and New Zealanders have still different robins of their own. The bobolink of the Northern states becomes the "rice bird" of the South, after the dressy males of springtime have changed into the plain brown plumage of winter. Some birds, however, have a variety of names in one district. Thus the eastern flicker is also a golden-winged woodpecker, a high-hole, a clape, and a yellow-hammer.

For formal reference purposes it is helpful to have one "official" vernacular name, and this the *Check-List of North American Birds*, published by the American Ornithologists' Union, endeavors to supply. (Not that *Check-List* names are invariably the best choices; many persons would prefer desert quail to "Gambel's quail," logcock to "pileated woodpecker," kestrel to "sparrow hawk," merlin to "pigeon hawk," etc. Our American sparrow hawk rarely catches sparrows, and the pigeon hawk probably never attacks pigeons!)

In this book we have followed the *Check-List*, with occasional references to local names possessing historic or folklore significance. It is interesting to consider the sources of a few names, mostly of American origin.

The place in which the bird lives accounts for such names as paisano (the Mexican name for the road-runner in the Southwest), chimney swift, alder flycatcher, barn swallow, Canada jay, cactus wren. The place where it was first discovered, perhaps by mere accident, gives us Cape May warbler, Tennessee warbler, Nashville warbler, Carolina parakeet. What it looks like or sug-

gests gives us upland plover (not a plover at all), snowy owl, ivory-bill, scissor-tail, white-eyed vireo, bluebird, black-throated blue warbler, meadowlark (not a lark), Baltimore oriole (the colors of a noble family), cardinal, indigo bunting, elf owl (minute size). How it acts or behaves yields fool hen, kingbird, butcher bird, mockingbird, cowbird (associated with cattle, as formerly with the bison).

From what it feeds on or how it feeds we get such names as sapsucker, pinyon jay, gnatcatcher. The last is, however, a sort of diminutive of "flycatcher" rather than an indication of a gnat diet. Some birds are named for or by individuals: for example, Kirtland's warbler, Swainson's hawk. Sometimes the voice suggests the name, as in mourning dove (but the mourning warbler is so called because it wears a dark hood), screech owl (a complete misnomer), sawwhet owl, chat. What the bird seems to say explains the names bob-white, chachalaca, killdeer, chuck-will's-widow, phoebe, pewee, chickadee, towhee. Where or how it nests accounts for burrowing owl, cliff swallow, ovenbird.

These are some of the main sources of bird names; the derivation of other names will be evident from descriptions in the text.

The Fate of America's Birds

The writings of the early European colonists in North America are filled with expressions of wonder at the wealth of life in the New World. This applied to the variety of trees in the forest (eight times as many as in Europe), to the fruit and flowers, the squirrels and deer, the lobsters and oysters, and perhaps most of all to the birds. It was natural that every toothsome wild fowl should have been considered a God-given resource, especially by Englishmen who came from a country where a man might be imprisoned for taking a pheasant's egg, or hanged for killing the deer of a landed proprietor. It was a welcome change to feel that wild turkeys, heath hens, partridges, pigeons, ducks, geese, swans, cranes, rails, and many smaller birds might be taken freely and without limit. Game was regarded as inexhaustible. But in America, the population was undergoing an amazingly rapid increase, and the changes in the character of the land deprived most birds and other wild animals of food and cover at the same time that they were being killed by every means and in every season.

The wild turkey, which dwelt only in America, was one of the first to become greatly reduced. The reason is plain, for a visitor to New Jersey in the year 1648 mentions a flock of 500 turkeys "got by nets" at one time! Fortunately, this splendid fowl has not altogether disappeared and is today even gaining in certain areas, despite the fact that the settlers in New England and the Middle Atlantic states quickly wiped it out along the Atlantic seaboard. Domestic turkeys, the descendants of birds that had been carried from Central America to Europe by the Spaniards, were brought back across the Atlantic to New England and New York at the very time when the local wild turkeys were disappearing. The Spanish colonists, by the way, were much more clever than the British in domesticating and cultivating all sorts of useful animals and plants of the New World.

Birds that have fared still worse are the Carolina parakeet, the heath hen or eastern prairie chicken, and the passenger pigeon. These were all abundant, but the last survivor of each has perished in the present century. The passenger pigeon used to travel in flocks that darkened the sky and took hours or days to pass a given point. It fed at certain seasons upon the nuts of the beech and the acorns of the white oak, and groves of these immense trees also furnished its nesting places. Passenger pigeons became such "common" food that servants and even slaves objected to eating them. Men laughed at the idea that the wild pigeons might ever become "scarce." Yet Audubon foresaw that the endless slaughter, combined with the cutting down of the oak forests, could not fail to be disastrous. The last passenger pigeon died in the zoo at Cincinnati in 1914.

Among remarkable North American birds that have become extremely rare because of less direct and possibly less wanton persecution are the ivory-billed woodpecker, the California condor, the whooping crane, and the trumpeter swan. The first of these is the "king of woodpeckers," larger than a crow, black and white, scarlet-crested, equipped with a white beak, and altogether the most spectacular member of the woodpecker family. The enormous chips it hews from trees infested with wood-boring insects have been likened to the work of a corps of axmen. Its existence depends upon stands of gigantic cypresses and similar trees, and unlike many birds, it does not tolerate the close presence of man. Following the clean sweep of the southern forests by lumbermen, it has all but vanished—which illustrates how the abuse of one aspect of life can work unforeseen damage upon others.

The whooping crane and the trumpeter swan have been brought almost to extinction by reduction of the range. The case of the California condor, largest of North American birds, is less clear. The condor is a harmless carrion eater of limited distribution, and its disappearance has to some extent resulted from poisoned carcasses set for bears and coyotes. But the thoughtless man with a rifle, ever ready to prove his marksmanship on a living target, shares the blame.

The best way to assure the preservation of our native birds is to "cultivate the range" for their benefit. This means that we must protect and extend a natural growth of vegetation that furnishes food and shelter. The artificial breeding of game birds is expensive, and food dished out by human hands is really useful only if the supply never fails. But wonders can be worked by encouraging suitable food plants, keeping wide hedges between tilled fields, and leaving a few dead trunks in the wood lot and a few tangles of undisturbed brush and thicket. A bed of sunflowers left to ripen will keep many birds busy for months. It has been found that if even a minute percentage of the growing grain is left unharvested, it will carry several coveys of quail through a hard winter.

A fair proportion of trees permitted to grow to full maturity greatly increases the number of birds. Old woodland, with normal undergrowth and forest-floor plants, has been found to support twice as many kinds of birds and five times as many resident families as young woods in which the undergrowth has been cut, burned, or grazed out. The living space of birds is, in other words, to be measured by cubic volume rather than by square area. The British Isles have not nearly so many species of birds as we, yet perhaps nowhere else in the temperate zone do birds seem to abound as in England. This is largely owing to the fact that the English people have wisely preserved so many of their vast and ancient trees.

Interest in birds and their conservation no longer requires any justification. It is hardly necessary to point out the economic importance of birds because of the insects they eat. Indeed, this particular value has been overemphasized. Many more kinds of insects are beneficial than are harmful, and birds seldom discriminate. But insects multiply at an incredible rate, and even "useful" forms become pests when they grow overabundant. The essential place of birds in nature's long chain of the eaters and the eaten is their part in keeping the delicate balance. The only birds that do not fit well into the balance are the foreign introductions, such as English sparrows and starlings; but this is true also of other forms of life that have been brought from abroad, such as house cats, carp, the Japanese beetle, the gypsy moth, many European weeds, and Old World organisms that cause plant diseases.

In primitive times the predatory animals — such as wolves, mountain lions, lynxes, weasels, eagles, hawks, and owls—existed in far greater number than in our own time. In spite of this, the plant eaters, the creatures we call game, the songbirds, and all other harmless and familiar animals flourished. Probably no wild bird or beast under natural conditions has ever exterminated another species or even seriously reduced its numbers. The flesh eater varies its diet; it kills off a greater proportion of the weak and the sick than of the strong; in addition, its food usually includes, as we have seen, enemies of the species upon which it relies for its living.

Only by exhaustive study can man determine which wild animals are beneficial and which destructive or undesirable, because the chains of relationship in nature are mostly complex and hidden from our view. In Georgia, where quail are fostered as game birds, it was formerly the custom of sportsmen to shoot marsh hawks at every opportunity because these predators sometimes kill quail. But the slaughter of marsh hawks seemed to accomplish nothing toward increasing the numbers of quail. Finally it was learned from the examination of stomach contents that the marsh hawk feeds mainly upon the cotton rat, a rodent highly destructive to the eggs of quail and other ground-nesting birds. A much greater foe of cotton rats than of quail, the marsh hawk has proved actually to be a *friend* of the quail.

It is not possible to save our birds, or the forests, the wild flowers, the life of river and sea, the game mammals, the fur bearers, or any other natural thing alone, because nature is a great unity. Any evil practice affecting one creature spreads out through the web of life and in the end affects many others. The goal must be to restore and maintain the closest approach to balanced nature that is consistent with the requirements of a large and ever-expanding human population.

The Introduction of Foreign Birds

Everybody knows that in North America there are a number of wild birds that did not arrive under their own power but were intentionally introduced by man. The starling and the English sparrow come to mind as the most "successful" examples, but there are also others, such as the ring-necked pheasant and the gray or Hungarian partridge. Even today some sportsmen yearn for the further introduction of game birds from various parts of the world. Grouse and pheasants of new kinds, tinamous, bustards, pigeons, terrestrial plovers such as the lapwing, and other species are mentioned as well adapted to this or that type of North American terrain in which the original game has been wiped out.

Fortunately, the wholesale importation and freeing of foreign species is no longer practiced. Even live birds transported for zoological parks and aviaries fall under the control and rigid scrutiny of the nation's Fish and Wildlife Service, and the privilege is not lightly granted. It was not always so. Despite our own wealth of native birds, our forefathers rather naïvely concluded that they could add skylarks, nightingales, missal thrushes, or any other creature to the charms of the temperate New World. "Acclimatization societies," the principal function of which was to introduce European birds and mammals, throve in American towns and cities until well after the middle of the nineteenth century. With a few—and those chiefly regrettable—exceptions, their efforts failed, for the reason that the ecological niches were already fully occupied by strongly intrenched native species. It is interesting, however, to consider a recorded instance of introducing songbirds from England.

Towards the end of 1852 the trustees of the Greenwood Cemetery in Brooklyn imported 168 British birds—48 skylarks, 24 wood larks, 48 British goldfinches, 24 European robins, 12 thrushes, and 12 European blackbirds—and freed them in the cemetery. The birds were purchased at an average price of eightpence, the entire importation costing slightly over one hundred dollars. The records of the cemetery state that the experiment was a failure because the freed birds all disappeared. Yet we know that skylarks were to be found for many years in fields on the outskirts of Brooklyn and that the British goldfinch still persists in the vicinity of Seaford and Massapequa, farther east on Long Island. Probably these birds are the descendants of those released so many years ago in the Greenwood Cemetery.

White-tailed Kites: A Painting by John James Audubon

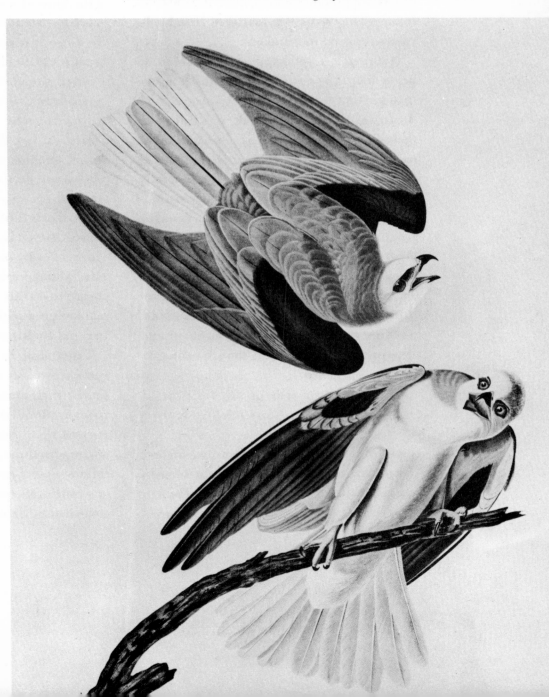

The tiny, and in this instance harmless, result of what was regarded a century ago as a rather large and commendable effort is an indication that human transfer of birds from one continent to another is likely to be futile, even if not objectionable.

Younger generations of Americans know little of our huge city populations of English sparrows about the turn of the century. At that date it seemed as though this alien species, by no means meek, was destined to inherit the earth. The birds subsisted mostly upon the oats in horse manure, and an era of gasoline motors ended their urban dominance. They remain as scattered farm birds, vastly reduced in numbers.

Nothing has yet happened, however, to bring about the downfall of the starling, the invader that followed the English sparrow. As an aggressive hole-nester, it is a too formidable rival of some of our best-loved native species, such as bluebirds and purple martins. Furthermore, as is not generally realized, the starling attains its worst status as a competitor on the winter feeding grounds. The food supply, whether insect or plant product, remains about as it was, but we now have ten foraging starlings to take the place of ten *different* native birds, including pipits, horned larks, cowbirds, grackles, meadowlarks, white-throated and tree sparrows, juncos, and snow buntings.

Observing and Studying Birds.

As Dr. Frank M. Chapman once wrote: "Birds are nature's most eloquent expression of beauty, joy, and freedom." Though relatively few persons can take up bird watching as a vocation, or even a serious avocation, those who are interested can find abundant opportunity to add to the sum of knowledge.

It is difficult for ornithologists to realize that most of their fellow men are entirely unaware of the variety of beautiful wild birds that live all around them. Even country residents are in many cases familiar only with the few that are large, conspicuous, or noisy—crows and jays, for instance—or those that are hunted—grouse, quail, and pheasants. Readers who first become acquainted with American birds through this book may wish to extend their study to living birds. To do so it is only necessary to go into the woods and fields, preferably in the season of spring migration, and to go as quietly as possible so that the birds may overcome any initial concern and resume their natural activities. For the smaller and more active kinds, such as warblers and kinglets, it is almost essential to be equipped with a pair of field glasses. By such means color and pattern can easily be scrutinized from a distance. Often it is possible to call birds within close range by imitating the cries of a frightened young bird. A "squeaker" that makes it easy to do this is now on the market. Owls can be lured within a few feet by those able to reproduce their calls at the correct pitch.

Proceeding in this way, one can learn to recognize many birds, whether or not one knows their names. But to most watchers, naming the birds will be an interesting aspect of their search. Part of the pleasure derives from the difficulties to be overcome. Of the several hundred species to be seen at one time of the year or another, a few of the conspicuous or otherwise distinctive kinds

24

can be identified at a glance by almost any-one. Others can be named with certainty only after careful observation, and a few present a challenge even to the experienced student.

The characteristics by which birds are recognized are far more numerous than might be supposed. One kind is told by its voice, another by its profile, another by the pattern of the plumage, and still others by color. Color is usually important and some-times is sufficient in itself. In eastern wood-lands a brilliant flash of scarlet amid the greenery can mean only one thing: a scarlet tanager. Sometimes a silhouette is more sig-nificant. To the trained eye the very differ-ent flight profiles of the black vulture and the turkey vulture distinguish the two at a glance; the fact that the head is black in one and red in the other is of little use because identification is usually accomplished at a distance so great that color is not visible. In some birds just one small detail may be all-important: the obscurely colored female of the black-throated blue warbler might easily be confused with a number of other species were it not for the presence of a small white check or spot at the base of the flight feathers.

The different plumages to be found in a single species may for a time confuse the observer. The male is often more brightly colored than his mate. In some birds the male is brightly colored in summer but molts in winter into a dull plumage like that of the female. In still others the adults of both sexes are alike but the young are differ-ent. Thus in many hawks the young are streaked below where the old birds are barred. The young of the bald eagle lacks the white head and tail so generally associ-ated with this species; it acquires them grad-ually after it is several years old. In the bobolink the handsome white, buff, and black male of summer is utterly unlike the brownish, sparrowlike hen bird. *All* bobo-links, however, have a metallic call note that is shared by no other American bird. Once this is learned, they can be detected even when migrating overhead at night.

Distribution and seasonal occurrence are also of major importance in identification. This is often a stumbling block to the begin-ner, who feels that because birds have the power of flight they may be expected any-where. We knew a successful chemist who made a hobby of "birding" for years but who nevertheless remained blithely una-ware that many of the species he continued to report from an eastern state were quite unknown there. And there was the lady who believed she had found a nest of the tree sparrow in New Jersey and could not under-stand our reluctance to accept her discovery. The tree sparrow has never been known to nest south of the subarctic zone! Of course, birds occasionally wander or are blown by storms far from their normal haunts. The identification of such rarities, however, is a matter best left to the expert, and even then the reports should not be accepted un-til corroborated by a number of observers or unless a specimen is collected and pre-served.

The time has passed in which collecting skins, eggs, or nests can accomplish anything of importance except in connection with special and unusual problems. North Amer-ican birds are nearly all well known as to description and range, and adequate collec-tions are preserved in museums. It is the living bird that now offers the most helpful opening for real research. The motto of *Audubon Magazine* stresses the fact: "A bird in the bush is worth two in the hand!"

Exactness and objectivity in making notes are more important than "fine writing." The great poets and naturalists of our own and earlier generations have given us a rich record of the impressions made by birds upon sensitive human beings; but scientific understanding of the basis of bird behavior has lagged. It is too easy to interpret birds as though they were human beings. They are highly instinctive creatures, with marvelous sense organs and bodily processes that proceed at a fast rate. Their pulse and respiration are more rapid than ours and their temperature considerably higher. On the other hand, their brains have none of the folded surface and very little of the "gray matter" that characterize the brain of a man or even of a dog. The mental processes of birds, indeed, seem more closely akin to those of lower vertebrates than of mammals.

How do birds respond in recognizing their own kind or other species, and in their courtship? What is the true meaning of their singing? Why their exclusiveness and jealousy regarding the private territory of breeding pairs? How does the internal "clockwork" of their bodies make them migrate at one season, build nests of a constant type at another, sit on eggs later, rear and then "heartlessly" abandon or drive away their fledglings? When we investigate such problems carefully, we soon realize that we are entering a field in which only precise and, if possible, statistical information is of service.

Enjoying wild birds is an activity in which

each may participate according to his circumstances. For those to whom birds, like flowers, are primarily a source of esthetic enjoyment, no detailed knowledge will be required, and it is only necessary to step into the woods or gardens and observe. By providing water and feeding stations and by planting fruit-bearing shrubs, birds can be induced to come to one's very windows. Observed under such advantageous conditions, it will be possible to identify, with the aid of the plates in this book, many of the better-known American birds.

With experience, one may wish to give more attention to the obscure or difficult species, and it is then advisable to possess one of the pocket guides concerned primarily with identification. Other books that record the habits and economic importance of each bird, in addition to hints on identification, will naturally be more bulky and hence not so suitable for use in the field. There are also many fine regional and state bird books.

Another way in which the beginning bird student can rapidly increase his knowledge, as well as the pleasure he derives from his hobby, is by joining a group with kindred interests. There are now bird clubs in almost all of our large and medium-sized cities. Many of these bear the name "Audubon Society" and have as their basic aim the preservation and conservation of birds and the natural environment. An organization of countrywide scope is the National Audubon Society, with headquarters in New York City. There are also technical ornithological societies, such as the Nuttall Ornithological Club of Boston, the Wilson Ornithological Club with headquarters in the Middle West, and the Cooper Ornithological Society on the Pacific Coast. The oldest and largest of such societies in America is the American Ornithologists' Union, a national group, which publishes a scientific journal, *The Auk,* founded in 1883. Both the National Audubon Society and the Fish and Wildlife Service of the Department of the Interior are outgrowths of the American Ornithologists' Union.

The Fish and Wildlife Service is prepared to assist the bird student in many ways. Over the course of the years this bureau has published numerous pamphlets on how to attract and recognize birds. One such bulletin, *Fifty Common Birds of Farm and Orchard,* illustrated in color by a gifted painter of birds, Louis Agassiz Fuertes, has awakened an interest in birds among hundreds of readers.

The Fish and Wildlife Service is also entrusted with the supervision of the now well-organized custom of bird-banding. To undertake this, one must first be able to identify one's temporary captives with certainty and be well acquainted with right and wrong methods, learned from the experience of bird banders in the United States and Europe. A permit to trap and band, numbered aluminum leg bands, and full instructions regarding cage traps, other equipment, and technique can be obtained by qualified individuals.

Hundreds of thousands of birds are now banded annually in the United States. The returns are surprisingly high, and a great deal has been learned about the routes and length of migration, the "homing" propensities of birds, the age to which they live, and their fidelity to individual mates. Banding and trapping enable an observer to *know,* instead of merely to guess, that the phoebe nesting on his porch was there last year. Many birds, such as the house wren, will stand almost any amount of proper handling, and so it is possible by catching them in their birdhouses to band all the residents of an entire district and to follow their complex family relationships from brood to brood and year to year.

The photographic displays in this book make it hardly necessary to add that photography provides another very popular approach to the enjoyment of birds. More and more persons are making movies and colored slides of wildlife in the out-of-doors for home enjoyment. The increasingly rigid restrictions placed upon gunning, because of growth in the human population and the rarity of certain game birds and mammals, is causing others to turn to photography as a more humane and rewarding form of outdoor activity. For those interested, Eliot Porter's "Notes on Bird Photography" on page 221 should prove helpful and rewarding.

Birds of Prey   1

Farmers and sportsmen often regard such birds as hawks with disapproval; yet we know that most birds of prey, as these are called, feed upon rats, mice, and other pests. They sometimes kill poultry and game, but even then may perform a service by eliminating birds that are feeble or sick. In a recent experiment involving many flights by homing pigeons, the pigeons were frequently attacked by hawks, but the only pigeon they caught was a runt—the weakest member of the flock.

Were it not for winged predators, such game birds as doves, partridges, and others might not have achieved the dashing flight and alertness which make them prized by sportsmen. When birds colonize remote islands where predators are absent, they often lose their speed and wariness and even the power of flight itself; witness the dodo, a giant flightless pigeon found only on a single small island in the Indian Ocean, where it was quickly exterminated after the arrival of man.

Entirely apart from economic considerations, there is an increasingly large group of citizens who believe that one of the antidotes to an overurbanized civilization is the preservation of recreational areas in an undisturbed condition, areas where the traveler and vacationist may observe and enjoy wild creatures. What better symbolizes the vigor of nature than a hawk soaring effort-lessly above ridge and canyon, or the plunge of a hunting eagle?

The bald eagle or American eagle (Plate 3), the national emblem of the United States, is a bird whose picture is recognized by most Americans, although very few have seen it in its wild state. Although now protected by a Federal statute, its large size makes it a tempting target for irresponsible riflemen and its numbers have continued to decline. At present this eagle is commonest at the two extremes of its range — Florida and Alaska—with smaller numbers living along the seacoasts and on the larger lakes and rivers inland.

The bald eagle belongs to a group known as sea or fish eagles. The feeding habits of these birds are hardly as dignified as their appearance, for their fare often consists of dead fish washed up on the beach. The bald eagle sometimes robs the hard-working fish hawk of its prey; occasionally it catches fish for itself or seizes wounded and crippled waterfowl. Benjamin Franklin understandably regretted the selection of this bird as the national emblem; however, it is imposing as it soars majestically through the air, its snow-white head and tail glistening in the sun. The huge nest, used and repaired year after year until it weighs hundreds of pounds, is a fitting home for such a bird.

The golden eagle (Plates 1, 2) ranges across the entire Northern Hemisphere but

Osprey

is rare in the eastern half of North America. With the exception of the massive wedge-tailed eagle of Australia, it is the largest of the true eagles of the genus *Aquila*, those birds of powerful hooked beak from which the word "aquiline" is derived. The eagles of this group have legs that are "booted" or densely feathered to the toes. They nest in trees or on cliffs and feed upon jack rabbits and large birds, but are not above supplementing their diet with carrion.

Although its great bulk imparts a certain deliberateness to the movements of the golden eagle, it has, when under way, tremendous speed and power. A pair of these eagles once took up residence at the Red Rock Refuge in Montana, where many waterfowl winter on the open water provided by thermal springs. Posting themselves in a grove of conifers above the valley, the eagles would catapult out after ducks that were flying from one spring to another. They rarely failed to strike their prey in mid-air.

The osprey, or fish hawk, well known along the less-frequented stretches of our seacoast, also visits large lakes and rivers inland. Almost the size of an eagle, it wheels slowly over the water until it spies a fish.

Then it plunges from a height of one hundred feet or more, entering the water with a great splash. The claws are sharp and the soles of its feet covered with prickly outgrowths, so that its slippery victim cannot escape.

The osprey sometimes places its bulky nest on the crossarms of a telephone pole, thus short-circuiting the wires. Tall poles with an old wagon wheel on top are commonly put up to provide it with a more suit-

Osprey

able platform for its nest. The osprey also nests on the ground in places where it will not be disturbed. Gardiner's Island, off the eastern end of Long Island, enjoys the greatest concentration of ospreys in the world, and at least one hundred of the resident pairs are ground-nesters. Not content with sticks, the osprey adds all sorts of objects to its nest—dried-up chicken wings, pieces of old tire, or lengths of rope. Its three or four large eggs are richly and handsomely marked with chocolate brown and in the old days were much prized by collectors. Such collectors are believed to have exterminated the osprey in the British Isles.

Kites

This old name refers to a group of hawks whose flight is particularly graceful and buoyant. In modern times the name has also been applied to the toy which, like one of these birds, hovers and bobs in the air. The kites are a rather diverse group, but they are known by their slender build and delicate feet, the latter suitable only for catching small or weak prey.

Old World kites are scavengers and even today swarm in the village streets of India. American kites do not share these habits, but catch their own food. The most specialized of this group is the everglade kite which, within the confines of the United States, can be seen in only a few of the larger marshes of Florida. It feeds exclusively on certain fresh-water snails of the genus *Ampullaria*; with its slender, curved upper mandible it pierces these in a nerve plexus, and the snail, soon rendered numb, virtu-

ally falls out of its shell. Although rare in the United States, the everglade or snail kite is common in certain marshes in tropical America and Cuba.

The swallow-tailed kite is another species found in Florida. Steel-blue above and pure white below, this kite has the proportions of a huge fork-tailed swallow. It spends much of its time floating effortlessly through the air, searching for large insects. It can snatch up small reptiles without interrupting its flight and devour them on the wing. The white-tailed kite is at present found within the United States chiefly in California. It may be recognized by its light, almost whitish plumage, and by its effortless hovering as it marks the location of a mouse on the ground below.

The lead-colored Mississippi kite is less beautiful than the two just mentioned but possesses the same graceful flight. A pair of these kites often perch on a tall dead tree and make long sallies after passing insects. This kite is a fairly common summer bird in many of the South Central States.

Harriers and Accipiters

The harriers are somewhat kitelike, with long wings and tail, and a flight that is light and buoyant. The only American harrier is the marsh hawk (Plate 4). As it courses at a low elevation over open country, its white rump is conspicuous. The only American hawk that regularly nests on the ground, it lays its bluish-white eggs beneath tall grass or low bushes in a secluded spot in a marsh. The adult male marsh hawk is a handsome

(Continued on page 49)

*Golden Eagle. The "golden" is
actually no more than a sheen
on the head and shoulders.*

2

1

*Golden Eagle. Found throughout
the Northern Hemisphere.*

3

*Bald Eagle. Exclusively
North American,
this imposing bird
has become our
national emblem.*

4

Marsh Hawk. One of the group known as harriers. It nests among reeds.

5

Pigeon Hawk. Captive young male.

Sparrow Hawk. Captive American kestrel, smallest and most common of our falcons.

6

7

Red-tailed Hawk. Lack of red in tail indicates a bird not fully adult.

8

*Red-tailed Hawk. One of the hawks
that soar on motionless wings. Often
mistakenly called "chicken hawk."*

9

*Broad-winged Hawk. A young
example of a good mouse-catcher.*

11

Sharp-shinned Hawk, Cooper's Hawk, and Goshawk. Three of the hawks that catch birds.

10

Sharp-shinned Hawk, Cooper's Hawk, and Goshawk (small to large). Captives trained for falconry.

12

Sharp-shinned Hawk. Though no larger than a blue jay, this fierce hawk is much feared by small birds.

13

Prairie Falcon. This pale desert bird nests on rocky mesas.

14

Peregrine Falcon or Duck Hawk. The bird
most prized by falconers everywhere.

15

*Prairie Chicken. Historic grouse
of western grasslands, now much
reduced in range and numbers.*

16

*Ring-necked Pheasant. Familiar game
bird brought here by way of Europe
from its original home in the Orient.*

*Ring-necked Pheasant. As with most pheasants the male is much
more colorful than the female. The species is polygamous.*

17

Ruffed Grouse. Widely distributed and best known of North American forest grouse.

19

Gambel's or Desert Quail. This rapid-running, fast-flying game bird is common along brush-lined creeks in the Southwest and in Mexico.

Chukar Partridge. Early attempts to introduce this handsome game bird into eastern and central United States failed; it now flourishes in Nevada.

20

21

Bob-white. The best-known quail, named after its cheery whistled call. Hunted as a game bird in the South, it is less common in the North and requires protection there.

22

Wild Turkey. Grandest of our native game fowl, unfortunately much reduced in numbers.

23

*Upland Plover, sometimes called
Upland Sandpiper. Really a
sandpiper and closely related
to the curlews.*

24

*Killdeer. This widely distributed member of the
plover family prefers open fields and golf links.
In autumn it commonly visits the seashore.*

25

*Spotted Sandpiper.
Found on sea beach,
pond shore, and
riverbank throughout
the United States.*

26

Burrowing Owl. Lives in prairie-dog burrows; only occasionally perches in a tree.

27

*Burrowing Owl. The Florida variety
on the family nest mound.*

28

*Great Horned Owl. When
hungry this fierce bird of
prey does not hesitate to
attack cats and skunks.*

29

*Long-eared Owl. A shy woodland
species that catches great
numbers of mice.*

30

*Short-eared Owl.
Unlike most owls,
this bird prefers
open marshes and
prairies, and nests
on the ground.*

31

Screech Owl fledglings. The thick woolly down that covers these baby owls is replaced by an adult form of feathering shortly after they are large enough to leave the nest and fly.

32

Screech Owl, gray phase. Gray and red plumage phases sometimes appear even in same brood.

33

Screech Owl, red phase.

34

*Barn or Monkey-faced Owl. This curious
bird nests in silos and church steeples
as well as in hollow trees.*

*Barn Owl and hungry brood. The most useful of all our owls, it
consumes vast quantities of mice and young rats.*

35

36

Snowy Owl. Nests on the ground in the Arctic, but in winter comes as far south as our northern states.

37

Saw-whet Owl. One of the smaller owls. Its note sounds like someone filing a saw.

38

*White-winged Dove. A favorite game bird in the
Southwest, it is rapidly becoming rare.*

39

*Mourning Dove. One of the most
common of our birds, it nests
in every part of the Union.*

40

*Inca Dove. A
southwestern bird
that prefers living
in villages or
on ranches.*

pearly gray. To impress his mate, he tumbles over and over through the air. Sometimes he brings a mouse, and the female flies up and catches it in mid-air as he drops it to her.

The three species of the genus *Accipiter*, the sharp-shinned hawk (Plates 10, 11, 12), the Cooper's hawk, and the goshawk, are among the few hawks that kill large numbers of birds. The sharp-shin catches small songbirds, the Cooper's hawk (Plates 10, 11) preys on medium-sized birds, while the large and formidable goshawk (Plates 10, 11) can be a scourge to grouse. All three of these species hunt in woods and seize their victims after a sudden dashing pursuit. Their wings are short and rounded, permitting them to thread their way through twigs and branches. They do not by any means feed exclusively upon birds; the Cooper's hawk and the goshawk catch many squirrels and chipmunks.

With its blood-red eye and handsome gray plumage, the adult goshawk embodies the wild qualities of the bird of prey. Even the immature birds, with their streaked plumage, have a fierce appearance. Because it has a steadier, more resolute disposition than its smaller cousins, the goshawk has long been used in falconry. It does not employ the spectacular dive or "stoop" of the falcon, but it is easily able to catch rabbits and grouse. Its tenacity is well known; it will sometimes chase rabbits through a briar patch on foot, or pursue chickens into their coop. This hawk is, moreover, the only American member of this family, not excepting the much larger eagles, which frequently launches a savage attack upon anyone attempting to climb to its nest or even approach the tree holding the nest. As with most birds of prey, the female goshawk is larger and fiercer than her mate.

Buteos

Hawks of this group are accomplished soarers; they are the broad-winged birds of prey seen wheeling slowly in great circles without a perceptible beat of the wings. In Britain they are called buzzards, a name that in America was unfortunately transferred to the turkey vulture. To the farm boy the soaring hawks are "chicken hawks"—birds to be shot at every opportunity, although, as a matter of fact, they live almost entirely upon harmful rodents, frogs, and even snakes. Of the three common species in the East, the red-tailed hawk (Plates 7, 8) is identified by its chestnut tail, the red-shouldered hawk by its preference for swampy woods and by the sharp white bands on its tail, and the smaller broad-winged hawk (Plate 9) by the fact that one of its white tail bands is much broader than the others. The broad-wing migrates in large flocks. Other species of hawks, though less sociable, also tend to concentrate during migrations, congregating along mountain ridges where updrafts permit them to soar lazily along on their journeys. At Hawk Mountain Sanctuary, near Drehersville, Pennsylvania, hundreds of hawks of several species can be seen on favorable autumn days.

Other North American buteos include the rough-legged hawk of the North, so called because it is feathered to the bases of its toes; the large light-colored ferruginous roughleg of the West; and the Swainson's

Everglade Kite

hawk, another common western species. The last-named bird, like several of its relatives, occurs in both dark and light color phases, so that identification must often be made on the basis of flight profile rather than color.

A few buteos of tropical America reach the southern limits of the United States. In the Southwest one may see the zone-tailed hawk, a species having a vulturelike flight profile; the stocky, water-loving Mexican black hawk; the small, grayish Mexican "goshawk" or gray hawk; and the handsome chestnut-shouldered Harris's hawk. The large white-tailed hawk of southern Texas and the little-known and rarely occurring short-tailed hawk of Florida complete this group.

Falcons

Falcons epitomize the "bird of prey." Bold and dashing in habits, they fly with unsurpassed speed, and easily capture other birds in full flight. The upper mandible of falcons has a well-developed notch which aids them in dismembering their prey. The gyrfalcon, the largest of the group, reaches a length of two feet.

The spectacular manner in which falcons overhaul and swoop upon their prey led to the development of the ancient sport of falconry. During the Middle Ages, falconry, which is as fixed and elaborate in its ritual as bullfighting, was the pastime of kings and nobility. The Emperor Frederick II of Hohenstaufen, whose treatise on falconry is still a valuable reference work, maintained hunting lodges throughout northern Italy, which he visited, according to the seasons, to engage in the sport. The various kinds of falcons were carefully distinguished, the two most highly prized being the bold peregrine or noble falcon, and the beautiful white gyrfalcon of the Arctic.

The goshawk and other species of less spectacular flight were used in hunting rabbits and similar game. In Central Asia the Mongols still use falcons and even golden eagles to aid their hunting expeditions, and in Lapland trained eagles are employed to bring the wolf to bay until the hunter can come up.

Falconry never quite died out, and it is now being revived in many parts of the world. It even intruded into world politics when Hermann Göring, bemedaled presi-

---

*The word "handsaw" is a corruption of "hernshaw" or "heron," and hence the adage is directly based upon falconry.

dent of the German hunting society, sent youths to Greenland to collect gyrfalcons for him, and also, some suggested, to make strategic observations. In 1952 a meeting of the German falconry society attracted many entries; the falcons were judged according to the perfection of their training and their success in hunting game. In America, too, falconry has some devotees, although it is often condemned by humane societies. Yet the meeting of man and bird when each is seeking an understanding of the other may have consequences as profound for the man as for the bird—as witness that remarkable book, *The Goshawk*, by T. H. White. In further defense of falconry, it may be argued that it brings the attractive qualities of the birds of prey to the attention of many who would otherwise consider them as mere pests.

Unfortunately, modern falconry does have undesirable aspects. Boys who do not know "a hawk from a handsaw"* swarm

Cooper's Hawk Feeding Young

Immature Swainson's Hawk

through the woods robbing nests of every kind of bird of prey, including many utterly unfitted for falconry. Valuable falcons are, for want of better facilities, staked out on the roofs of city apartments, often to die of inexpert handling. Would-be falconers steal young peregrine falcons from nests in state parks, and the few pairs of this species, the "noble falcon" of antiquity, that nest in the more settled parts of the East are driven away from their ancestral homes.

The peregrine (Plate 14) is found almost everywhere in the world. In America it is usually known as the duck hawk or, in some areas, the great-footed hawk. It nests on cliff ledges, often near water. The male scratches away the gravel to make a little depression, the so-called "scrape," and in this his mate lays three or four reddish-brown eggs. Having learned that city pigeons furnish easy fare during the winter, the peregrine sometimes perches atop a skyscraper and launches attacks on pigeons below. On occasion, falcons have even nested on high ledges of city buildings. The bird is easily recognized by the bold black marks or "mustaches" on the sides of the head. The prairie falcon (Plate 13) of the West might be described as a pale-colored peregrine.

The merlin, or, as it is called in America,

the pigeon hawk (Plate 5), is a compact little falcon, smaller than a pigeon. It is fully the equal of its larger cousins in dash and spirit but limits itself to such prey as dragonflies and swallows, which it is adept at catching in full flight. It snaps up the big insects with its bill and then transfers them to its talons. The merlin usually builds a platform nest in a tree but sometimes nests on the ground on a steep hillside, beneath low evergreens and bracken. As in other falcons, the male is considerably smaller than its mate. The species nests in the North and ranges over most of the continent in migration.

The gyrfalcon is a bird of the Arctic. Some individuals are white, others gray or blackish, with both types known to occur in the same brood. Even in midwinter, relatively few gyrs get as far south as the northern border of the United States.

The sparrow hawk, or American kestrel (Plate 6), is the smallest falcon in this country. It is the commonest hawk in the United States, because its small size exempts it from some of the senseless persecution to which the group is subjected. Both sexes of this handsome species have a chestnut-colored tail, but the slaty back distinguishes the male from the brown-backed female. These differences become apparent in the young birds as soon as their first feathers have grown in. The brown tail separates it from the pigeon hawk, the only other small falcon.

The sparrow hawk nests in a hole in a tree. The eggs are brownish, like those of open-nest falcons, and not white like those of most hole-nesting birds. The closely related European kestrel lays its eggs in an open nest in a tree. The sparrow hawk sometimes catches sparrows, especially the vexatious house sparrow, but the bulk of its food consists of mice and large insects. It has a habit of hovering in the air before pouncing upon its prey. Sparrow hawks occur throughout both North and South America.

Within the borders of the United States, Audubon's caracara is common only in the Everglades of Florida. It is abundant in Mexico, where it runs alongside the highways almost like a chicken, for its legs are long and strong. Although the caracara has an imposing, flat-headed, aquiline profile, it is a member of a rather degenerate group of falcons whose members have the feeding habits of vultures.

Vultures

Vultures the world over have had an age-long relationship with man because of their role as scavengers and eaters of carrion. Most of the many references to the "eagle" in the English Bible are believed to be mistranslations of words meaning vulture. Actually, the African and other Old World vultures are rather closely related to eagles and hawks, despite their remarkable resemblance in appearance and habits to New World vultures. The latter belong to a quite distinct family.

Both the Eastern and the Western Hemisphere groups are extraordinarily accomplished fliers, particularly adept in the art of soaring. On set and upcurved wings, with the tips of the primaries fingered out, they take every aerodynamic advantage of the rising currents of air known as thermals and, in the search for their sparsely distrib-

Captive Immature Red-shouldered Hawk

Immature Western Red-shouldered Hawk

uted food, cover vast areas with a minimum of effort. Most naturalists believe that they hunt by sight and that the descent of one bird to earth starts the chain reaction that brings others from wider and wider circles to the carcass at the hub.

There is an old and controversial difference of opinion as to whether American vultures have, as is popularly believed, a keen sense of smell. Audubon, who was one of the first to use the turkey vulture in experiments, concluded that they did not.

More recent studies suggest that the turkey vulture has a fairly well-developed olfactory sense, whereas the black vulture is in this respect less well-equipped. Where both species are found together, it is noteworthy that the black vultures usually fly high, leaving the low-level search of the ground to the turkey vultures. Then, when the latter have located carrion, the black vultures descend like pirates to share or appropriate it. Most vultures of both the New and Old Worlds avoid densely wooded areas, and

Turkey Vulture

occur chiefly in relatively open country — savannah, plain, desert, or seashore. This supports the theory that in their hunt for food they rely mainly upon sight.

When the British first settled in what was later to become the southern part of the United States, they applied to two conspicuous soaring birds the name buzzard, which properly belongs to a common European hawk, a relative of our red-tail. Nevertheless, turkey buzzard and black buzzard are now accepted American vernacular.

The turkey vulture, which has a bare, reddish head and neck together with blackish-brown plumage, is a race of a species distributed from Canada to Cape Horn. It is commonest in the Southern states, but its breeding range extends well to the north in the interior of the continent. Lately, it has also spread rather rapidly up the Hudson Valley and across the Canadian border in the middle of the continent. It nests on the ground, laying two eggs among rocks or within a stump, often taking to a patch of woodland for concealment during its period of reproduction.

Heavier, bolder, more aggressive on the ground, the black vulture loses its advantage in the air, where it is less accomplished than the turkey vulture. The best way to distinguish between the two at long range is not by the black plumage, head, and neck, nor by the more conspicuous white patch on the wings of this species, but rather by the way the black vulture frequently interrupts its planing flight with three or four quick, seemingly labored wingbeats.

The range of the black vulture is more southerly or subtropical than that of the turkey vulture. The habits of the former bring it into close association with man. Before the era of modern sanitation, droves of black vultures lived about the garbage dumps of many southern cities, effectively disposing of all sorts of offal, as they still do in Latin America. Their food does not need to be rotten, but apparently no degree of putrefaction can render it unpalatable to them.

The California condor, a magnificent North American vulture, is one of the largest land birds in the world. With a wing ex-

panse of about ten feet, it equals in size the Andean condor and the biggest of the Old World birds of prey, and is exceeded among flying birds only by the greatest albatrosses. An even larger condor once lived in the area that is now the Southern states, but that was in the Ice Age, and that condor is known to modern man only from its bones.

In view of the alarming rarity of the California condor, which is now confined to two counties in the southern part of that state, where it is supposed to be rigidly protected, the old accounts of its huge numbers are astounding. In early days the normal mortality of a vast population of large mammals provided these birds with abundant food. With the settlement of California, the great birds were shot, or they were accidentally destroyed when they devoured bodies of animals that had been poisoned in order to eliminate wolves and bears. Now only a few remain, nesting on high ledges of wild and arid canyons, and earnest effort will be required to prevent their total extinction.

Black Vulture Leaving Nest

Turkey Vulture at Nest

Upland Game Birds   2

This large and important group contains such familiar birds as chickens, pheasants, quail, grouse, and turkeys. The true pheasants and partridges are natives of the Old World but a few of them were brought to America as game birds and are now widely distributed. Such others as the turkey and the quail of the bob-white group are indigenous in the Western Hemisphere. America has its share of that much-admired northern game bird, the grouse. Of the interesting tropical American game birds known as guans and curassows, only one species reaches the United States, the chachalaca, which appears in the lower Rio Grande Valley of Texas. This bird's noisy cries, uttered at morning and evening, resemble the syllables *cha-cha-la-ca*.

Quail

The bob-white (Plate 21) is the best-known of American quail, partly because it tells its name so loudly. It is a plump bird about a foot long, partial to brush fields, where coveys, each containing a dozen or so birds, live together during autumn and winter. With the advent of spring, the flocks break up into pairs, each of which attempts to rear a large brood of young. Unlike most game birds, the male bob-white takes a genuine interest in his family.

In the colder parts of the United States, the bob-white has a difficult time during hard winters. Its numbers become so depleted that hunters often completely eliminate the few that remain. For this reason, and because of its cheery song and useful habits, the bob-white has been placed on the protected "songbird" list in some Northern states.

The bob-white ranges south into Mexico, where it shows much variation in color from area to area. One that the authors observed feeding fearlessly beside a boulevard in the city of Vera Cruz was almost brick red. One of the most interesting of these southern varieties is the masked bob-white, formerly found in southern Arizona. Destruction of its native grassland by overgrazing exterminated it in the United States; it is said to survive in some of the more remote sections of the Mexican state of Sonora.

Other American quail are all restricted to the western, and chiefly to the southwestern, parts of the United States. Best known is the California quail, with its handsome feathered topknot that springs from the forehead and curls forward. It is common and, where protected, lives tamely around ranches. The Gambel's quail, or desert quail (Plate 19), a closely related species, abounds in brushy areas in Arizona and adjacent parts of Mexico. The mountain quail, a very attractive bird native to the foothills of California and Oregon, is little known because of its fondness for thick chaparral, to which it clings except when forced to take wing. The scaled quail, found in the brushy plateaus of the Southwest and in Mexico, is a trim bird with a whitish topknot. Another species that crosses our southern borders

California Quail

only in some of the remote mountains of the Southwest is the Montezuma quail, or, as it is sometimes called, the Mearns's quail or "fool" quail. The last name comes from the fact that its curiously streaked and banded head gives it a clownish aspect. The breast is black and the back checkered with white, gray, and black. This is another of the numerous grassland birds that have suffered from the effects of overgrazing.

Old World Partridges

The Old World partridges are plump game birds, intermediate in size between quail and pheasants. Two species have be- come established in the United States, the gray or Hungarian partridge and the chu- kar partridge. The former is common over most of Europe. The stock that was brought to America supposedly came from Hungary; hence the wide use of the name Hungarian partridge in this country.

The Hungarian partridge can exist in cultivated country better than most native American game birds. When flushed it flies very rapidly and vigorously with a sharp clatter of wingbeats. As it scales or glides to a landing, it may be recognized by the chestnut-colored tail feathers. It is espe- cially common in the wheat fields of west- ern Canada.

The chukar partridge (Plate 20) is wide-

Mountain Quail

Female Scaled Quail

spread in the drier parts of the foothills of the Himalayas in northern India. Efforts to introduce it into the United States were unsuccessful for many years, but it has recently found the bleak mountain ranges of Nevada to its liking. The chukar is an attractive game bird, with a black crescent on the breast and black and chestnut bars on the sides.

Pheasants

The true pheasants, a group which includes the peacock and the jungle fowl, the latter being the ancestor of domestic chickens, are birds of unsurpassed brilliance of plumage. The common pheasant has been introduced in many parts of the world, including Europe and America. The American stock came for the most part from a Chinese variety that has a white collar and is known as the ring-necked pheasant (Plates 16, 17). It is now common over most of the northern United States and in southern Canada. Hundreds of thousands are shot every year, but it still thrives. The cock pheasant, despite his brilliant colors, can hide in dense cover and brambles very cunningly and is adept at running before a dog until far enough ahead to fly away safely. Since the species is polygamous, restriction of shooting to the male birds saves the hens for reproduction.

The hen pheasant lacks the bright colors of her mate. She is inconspicuously streaked

61

White-tailed Ptarmigan in Winter Plumage

with brown and gray and is almost invisible as she sits on her clutch of ten or twelve eggs in a nest concealed on the ground. The cock does not help in the incubation of the eggs or in the care of the downy chicks. The crowing of the male pheasant is like that of his domesticated cousin, the barnyard rooster, except that he utters a loud two-syllabled cry and then flaps his wings, whereas the rooster flaps his wings and then crows.

Turkeys

Turkeys are unmatched as game birds. They represent America's most important contribution to the roster of domestic animals, because the various forms evolved in the Western Hemisphere and were unknown in Europe until Spanish monks transported to Europe a stock that had already been domesticated by Indians in Mexico. The curious name "turkey" is due to a misunderstanding regarding the identity and source of the first living domesticated examples, introduced into Great Britain from the Mediterranean area.

Our British forebears, unlike the Spanish and Portuguese settlers of Central and South America, were not good domesticators and acclimatizers of plants and animals useful to man. They shot and trapped the native turkeys over the greater part of the ancient range and ultimately received the Mexican barnyard variety by way of Europe. Recently, as a result of wise laws and public sentiment, the eastern turkey has regained a small portion of its old numbers and territory.

Five closely related subspecies of the fowl that has been dedicated to Thanksgiving Day live in North America. One of them, the eastern turkey, ranges throughout forested country from Ontario southward to northern Florida, westward beyond the Mississippi, and well into Mexico.

Wild turkeys (Plate 22) consort in flocks both before and after the breeding season. They are polygamous and, following mating, the hens lay large sets of speckled eggs in secluded ground nests and rear the family without assistance from the dominating gobbler. They feed on insects, fruits, and such mast as white-oak acorns, and are always ready to raid an isolated cornfield. They are extremely wary and shrewd, but often do not recognize a human being who approaches on horseback or in a horse-drawn vehicle. At night they seek roosting places in trees, preferably in impassable swamps. Although they spend little time on the wing, they are strong fliers. The authors have seen them, after being flushed, rise swiftly above the tops of southern pines, or zoom across broad rivers of the Carolina Low Country.

Grouse

The eighteen species of grouse are native to the Northern Hemisphere. They are rather closely related to the pheasants, but their coloration is less brilliant. Since no member of the grouse family has been domesticated, they are important chiefly as game birds.

In eastern North America the ruffed grouse, or partridge (Plate 18), is known as

White-tailed Ptarmigan in Summer Plumage

the king of upland game birds. It bursts into flight with a disconcerting roar of powerful wings and speeds away recklessly through bushes and trees. Sportsmen find it a difficult target, and even the most expert wing shots seldom score an authentic "double."

The range of the ruffed grouse extends across southern Canada and southward in the western mountains to California but its real headquarters is in the northeastern United States. Its numbers fluctuate greatly from year to year, following to some extent a ten-year cycle of abundance. The cause of these cycles is still uncertain, one theory being that epidemic diseases break out when the grouse population exceeds a certain density. In the spring the cock grouse seeks out a log and "drums" to attract a mate; he produces this drumming by whirring or beating his wings so rapidly that they seem a mere blur. Like most members of the family, the ruffed grouse is nonmigratory. In cold winter weather it is reduced to eating hemlock needles, rose hips, and other emergency fare. At such times it often plunges into a deep, soft snowbank to spend the night. Thus insulated, it remains warmer than if it were roosting on a limb exposed to the wind.

North of the range of the ruffed grouse in the arctic tundra lives the hardy ptarmigan. One species, the white-tailed, ranges southward in the Rocky Mountains as far as New Mexico but is restricted to the bleak alpine meadows above timberline. The most remarkable fact about ptarmigans is their seasonal change in color. In summer they are brown, matching the ground on which they live, feed, and nest. In winter, when the tundra is covered with snow, they molt into a pure white garb. They are thus camouflaged as a protection from foxes and snowy owls.

The blue grouse, a group which includes the sooty grouse and Richardson's grouse, live in the great coniferous forests of western North America. In the spring the male perches on a lofty limb and produces a loud hooting by inflating and deflating air sacs on his neck.

The dark-colored spruce grouse is an inhabitant of the dense paper-pulp woods of Canada and the northern United States. Its flesh tastes too strongly of spruce to be very palatable; nevertheless, this "fool partridge," as it is sometimes called, is so fearless—or foolhardy—that it has become rare except in the more remote parts of its range.

Prairie Grouse

The plains of interior North America are the home of a group of prairie grouse not found anywhere else in the world. There are four species—the lesser prairie chicken, the greater prairie chicken, the sharp-tailed grouse, and the sage hen. The prairie chicken (Plate 15) is the best-known of these. Its range once included all the Middle Western states, and a race known as the heath hen formerly lived in the open, burned-off brushy or grassy areas of southern New England, Long Island, and New Jersey. The heath hen is now extinct, and the prairie chicken is sadly depleted in numbers.

The sharp-tailed grouse is allied to the prairie chicken but prefers poorer, sandy

(Continued on page 81)

41

Yellow-billed Cuckoo. Respectable member of a family notorious for parasitism. Its own nest is a flimsy one.

42

Black-billed Cuckoo. Like the yellow-bill, but without chestnut-colored wings and white-tipped tail.

43

Road-runner. Although a weak flier, it can run down and catch lizards and small snakes.

Whip-poor-will. Superbly camouflaged as it covers its two eggs.

44

45 *Black-chinned Hummingbird. Caught by the high-speed camera as it probes for nectar.*

46

*Broad-tailed Hummingbird.
The male flashes his gorget.*

47

Black-chinned Hummingbird. Although the male does not help, his mate may raise many broods.

48

*Anna's Hummingbird.
Seen in California
all through the year.*

49

*Rivoli's Hummingbird.
A large species, rare
in this country.*

50

*Broad-billed Hummingbird.
Like all hummers this one
sucks nectar through its
tubular tongue and eats
tiny insects.*

51

*Costa's Hummingbird. Very small
but very pugnacious.*

52

*Rufous Hummingbird.
A species that reaches
Alaska, here caught
in a pose showing how
it is streamlined for
high-speed flight.*

53

Belted Kingfisher. Young bird just out of the nest.

54

Coppery-tailed Trogon. A brilliantly colored tropical species. In the United States, found only in Arizona.

Golden-fronted Woodpecker. Found in Texas and Mexico, particularly near rivers, it is one of the commonest and noisiest birds in such areas.

55

56

Cactus Woodpecker.
A small desert-dwelling
woodpecker, like the
downy of the East in
appearance and habits.

57

Red-headed Woodpecker. Feeds on
insects and ripe berries.

Red-bellied Woodpecker. Its trilling cry resembles that of tree frog.

58

59

Lewis's Woodpecker. A characteristic sight in the West is this beautiful bird darting from a perch on a dead tree to catch insects on the wing. Mexicans call it Carpintero Negro, the "black carpenter."

60

Pileated Woodpecker. A powerful bird of crow size, it is the largest woodpecker in the North.

61

Gila Woodpecker. Named for the Gila River of Arizona. Sometimes called desert woodpecker, it often digs a nesting burrow in the stem of a giant cactus.

62

Yellow-bellied Sapsucker. Drills holes in the bark of trees and drinks the flow of sweet sap.

63

Acorn Woodpecker. So called because it stores acorns in holes which it drills in bark. Also called California woodpecker and ant-eating woodpecker.

64

Eastern Flicker. Feeds on ants.

Downy Woodpecker. Tamest and smallest of the woodpeckers.

65

66

Red-shafted Flicker. The name "flicker" is derived from one of the many call notes of these noisy birds.

67

*Eastern Kingbird. Generally tranquil at its nest but known
to fight hawks and crows belligerently.*

Western Kingbird. The parents feed the young birds on insects caught on the wing.

68

69

Say's Phoebe. Like all phoebes, a member of the flycatcher family. It inhabits arid regions in the West, usually building its nest in a hole in a bank, an empty well, or a chink in a wall. It lays four or five pure white eggs.

70

Eastern Phoebe. Hardier than other flycatchers, this one returns north early in the spring.

71

Black Phoebe. This western bird, closely related to the eastern species, is always found near water.

Wood Pewee. Its plaintive song, resembling the syllables "pee-wee," is a familiar sound in shady eastern woods during the summer months.

72

areas, partly overgrown with brush. After the great pine forests of Wisconsin and Michigan were logged off, the sharptail moved in. A few decades later, when the brush had grown into good-sized aspens or birches, the sharptail was crowded out, to be replaced by the woodland-loving ruffed grouse.

The males of both the prairie chicken and the sharptail gather in the spring on community display grounds or *leks*. Here the cocks produce their booming challenges, and each fights to establish a little domain of his own. Most of the conflicts are stylized sham battles, involving much sparring and bluffing. Some of the dances of the Plains Indians are imitations of the dancing grouse.

The most remarkable of the open-country grouse is the sage hen of Wyoming and Utah. The male struts about grotesquely with yellow throat patches inflated, and spinelike tail and breast feathers puffed out. By suddenly deflating the air sacs on his neck, he makes a ludicrous noise. So engrossed does the male become with his love-making that the coyote is sometimes able to approach stealthily within leaping distance.

Plovers and   3
Sandpipers

The shore-bird group is a large one, distributed throughout the world, including such inhospitable areas as the Antarctic.

Most of the species are associated with salt water, but there are some that have become virtually dry-land birds. These upland species are the only ones that come within the scope of this book. They include the killdeer, woodcock, upland plover, and spotted sandpiper.

Historically, the snipes and plovers were famous as game birds, but in this role they are not fitted by nature to compete with ducks and grouselike birds. The shore birds lay small sets of eggs (four or fewer). The bulk of them follow narrow, coastwise migration routes, where they are likely to run an endless gantlet of gunners. And finally, they are less wary than the ducks and the grouse. For such reasons, nearly all of them have been removed in recent years from the list of game birds in the United States, and their numbers have since that time shown a gratifying increase.

The killdeer (Plate 24), a universal favorite, became a farm bird with the settlement of the continent. It now probably nests in every state of the Union as well as throughout the southern part of Canada. It is, furthermore, a hardy neighbor, staying well into cool autumn, and a few even wintering as far north as British Columbia, Illinois, and New York. Its piping call, *kill-dee, kill-dee,* is one of the most nostalgic-sounding songs of the countryside. Killdeers flock during much of the year but break up into pairs at nesting time. The comical chicks that hatch from the four large, protectively colored eggs run rapidly over the ground when discovered, looking like balls of fluff on matchsticks. When danger threatens, the parents put on a tragic-looking wounded-bird performance,

Male Sage Grouse Displaying

dragging the wings and showing their bright, almost orange, rump patches. In spite of their intimacy with man, killdeers never seem to become really friendly.

Woodcocks are the most prized game birds among the shore birds, both in North America and in the Old World. The American species is slightly smaller than its counterpart in Europe, but the habits of the two are much alike. The woodcock is a bird of damp places, rather than of water. It is an eater of earthworms, which it captures by thrusting its long bill into the soil, thus making the holes that are telltale of its feeding area. Just how it locates its prey—by hearing, scent, or the tactile sense—has long

been the subject of a controversy. There are even observers who insist that the woodcock first punches its holes and then returns to pull out the earthworms that have entered them! Whatever the facts may be, its bill is an efficient, flexible extractor. By exerting muscles that change the angle of the quadrate bone at the base of the jaw, the bird bends the tip of the upper mandible into a hook and draws up the worm until it can be grasped and swallowed. The bird's eyes are placed well toward the back of its head, which permits it to keep a sharp lookout even with its face in the mud!

Woodcocks come north from winter quarters as soon as the soil has thawed. The incubating female is not infrequently covered by late snowfalls. The courtship proceedings are dramatic, involving towering flights by the males in early evening, during which their wings whistle melodiously. Both before and after these flights, they utter a nasal call, usually written as *peent*. Adults, eggs, and young are all colored so amazingly like the lights and shadows of the forest floor that woodcocks rely on their camouflage and do not flush readily. It is sometimes possible even to touch a mother bird on the eggs before she will pop off, walk away in leisurely fashion, lift her tail like a fan, and flash the silvery white undercoverts, the only really conspicuous markings in the whole plumage. On migration, woodcocks

make mass nocturnal flights. It is these, in autumn, that gunners watch and hope for during the open season.

The upland plover (Plate 23) is not a plover at all, but is a sandpiper that has a somewhat ploverlike bill and much of the manner of a plover. Its taste in habitat, for example, is similar to that of the killdeer, which is a true plover. Unfortunately, the friendly human sentiment that has protected the killdeer has done little for the upland plover. The species was so extensively and ruthlessly shot during the long period in which shore birds were legal game that it has become rare and is now perhaps in danger of extinction. At one time gunners walked abreast of horse-drawn wagons over

Male Sharp-tailed Grouse Displaying

grasslands, a trick that caused the upland plovers to be slow to take alarm. On such occasions, the wagons were often loaded with their bodies.

The nesting habits of the upland plover are much like those of the killdeer, except that it prefers grassier areas. While sailing above its nesting grounds, it utters a beautiful, plaintive whistle. Unlike the killdeer, it leaves the United States in winter and makes a tremendously long migration into the Southern Hemisphere. This results in its undoing, because, although legally protected in the United States and Canada, it may be shot on the grassy pampas of Argentina.

The little spotted sandpiper (Plate 25), the "teeter" of every pond, lake, stream, bay, river, and ocean beach, is probably familiar to more persons than are any other species of the group. The spotted thrushlike breast in spring and early summer is distinctive, as is also the curious flight in which irregular, short, fluttering beats of the wings

Female Dusky Grouse

are followed by glides. Although its tipping or teetering habit is shared with certain larger snipes, this nervous-looking reaction, of uncertain function, is probably most pronounced in the spotted sandpiper. In many parts of South America, the teeter is called *tiltil*, which has the same meaning.

The extraordinary attribute of the spotted sandpiper is its ability to fit comfortably into many diverse habitats. Water, salt or fresh, warm or cold, flowing or stagnant, on the coast or in the middle of the continent, seems to suit it equally well. It is similarly adaptable in its winter home, for the writers have encountered it along mangrove-bordered tropical rivers of Central and South America, on surf-beaten rocks on the desert coast of Peru, and tipping along the margins of lofty and icy lakes in the Andes.

Owls 4

Owls feed on small mammals, frogs, and other birds, and are therefore classed, along with hawks and falcons, as birds of prey. Actually, however, owls are not related to hawks. Most owls are active only or chiefly at night and, though it may be more difficult to hunt in darkness, this is apparently offset by the fact that many of the animals they catch, such as rats and mice, are more active then.

Owls vary greatly in size, but all have sharp claws or talons, as they are called.

Barred Owl

Two of the four toes extend forward and two backward, and are thus especially useful in seizing and grasping the prey. The eyes are large and are directed forward; the entire head is quickly rotated when the owl wishes to look to one side or to the rear. The ear openings are much larger than in most birds and an owl's hearing is extremely keen. Many owls have a little tuft of feathers projecting up from each side of the forehead; these are called horns or ears. Owl feathers are very soft and owl flight is almost noiseless. Female owls are larger than males, a characteristic which they share with hawks. Owls bolt their prey, feathers, fur, and all.

The indigestible parts are then coughed up or regurgitated as pellets. The pellets of each kind of owl are so dissimilar from those of all other kinds that most species can be identified from the pellets alone. Study of the food of owls has been undertaken chiefly through dissection and examination of such pellets.

The barn owl, or monkey-faced owl (Plates 34, 35), is beautifully variegated with buff and gold. It is one of the most widely distributed of all birds and has become associated largely with man-made structures, such as farm buildings, unused garrets, and the housings of water tanks.

85

Much of its prey is also brought within its reach by man, the various kinds of rats and mice that accompany human settlement making up a great part of its food. The bushel or so of brown rat skulls ejected in pellets during the rearing of a family of comical-visaged young barn owls is quite astounding and is convincing evidence of the extraordinary usefulness of this species. In wilder areas the food includes native rodents, such as the pestiferous western gophers and ground squirrels.

The barn owl remains in close concealment throughout the day, and the moment of its evening foray is determined very exactly by fading light. For example, on seven June days before the summer solstice—that is, while the period of daylight was still lengthening—it was observed that a barn owl arrived at a farmyard near Poughkeepsie, New York, a minute or two later in the dusk of each successive evening. The bird always heralded its approach with a series of soft quacking or clucking notes.

The screech owl (Plates 31, 32, 33), probably the best-known North American species, is an eared owl, with an erect tuft of feathers above each eye. It is what biologists call a plastic bird because its populations can be divided according to size, or hue of plumage, into fifteen North American geographical races, each of which belongs to a particular climatic niche. These various forms cover the continent from tropical Mexico to southern Alaska and from semi-desert areas to the northwestern coastal rain forest.

Most of the races of the ordinary screech owl are dichromatic, which means that their plumage may be of a reddish or a grayish phase. The difference has no relation to age or sex; the young birds of a single brood, in fact, often exhibit each type of feathering.

Screech owls inhabit remote wildernesses, of course, but they also take well to rural areas and even to parks and suburbs, where their quavering nocturnal cries are familiar. An imitation of their call will often lure them into close range, but it is easier to spot their silhouettes against the sky than to hear them, for they move on absolutely noiseless wings. In the period when the parents are taking fledglings on their first evening hunts, it is not difficult to stalk one of the unsophisticated youngsters from the rear and grasp it as it sits on a low limb. Its snapping beak may be disregarded as harmless, but not so its claws! And the stalker should not be surprised if one of the parents flies straight into his face in defense of its baby.

Screech owls are cavity dwellers, with a predilection for holes chipped out by flickers or other large woodpeckers. The race inhabiting the northeastern United States seems especially partial to the nesting places provided by old apple orchards. It will also accept birdhouses if they have sufficiently large entrances. Mice and other small mammals make up the bulk of the screech owl's food, but it also picks off small birds asleep on their perches and further varies its diet with insects, spiders, scorpions, crayfish, lizards, amphibians, and even fish.

The great horned owl (Plate 28) is a sort of giant brother of the screech owl, being of similar conformation, ear-tufted, and yellow-eyed. It, too, is a species with many geographical races. These races reveal the

Young Great Horned Owl

relationship between pigmentation and climate, for the dusky horned owl of the moist Pacific forests between Alaska and northern California is very dark, the western horned owl of the treeless country between central Texas and southeastern California is pale, and the arctic horned owl, which breeds northward to tree limit around Hudson Bay and in the Mackenzie River Valley, is as whitish as many examples of its northern cousin, the snowy owl.

The great horned owl is an extremely powerful and rapacious creature, capable of killing relatively large birds and mammals. It is the only owl really dreaded by gamekeepers and poultrymen. Rabbits probably furnish the bulk of its food in most areas, but it often attacks skunks, apparently not the least intimidated by a weapon that is so thoroughly effective against man, fox and even bear. An appreciable number of great horned owls skinned by collectors have been found to carry the lingering taint of encounters with skunks. This bird has also been known to eat young porcupines—quills and all.

The great horned owl usually nests in the open but does not build its own home. An old nest of a squirrel, a crow, a large hawk, or a heron will serve its purpose. In Florida it lays its two or three big white eggs as early as December, and in the northeastern United States before the end of February. There is even a tale of eggs taken from an Alaskan nest in April that froze solid by the time they reached ground level! Because of the fearlessness and ferocity of the great horned owl, the ascent to a nest is not to be undertaken lightly. The adults, especially the big, savage female, sometimes at-

tack anyone attempting to climb to the nest, though more often than not they fly meekly away.

The great horned owl is active at night and as a rule utters its deep-voiced and memorable hoot only in the dark hours. It sees well by day, however, and on dark winter days often begins hunting in the late afternoon.

The snowy owl (Plate 36), a large round-headed species—that is, without horns or ear tufts—nests throughout the Arctic. Since its home is in "the land of little sticks" it nests on the ground, making a bed of moss and feathers on the open tundra for its six to eight, or more, white eggs. The cold forces immediate and continuous incubation, and it is said that the chick from the first egg may be well feathered before the last egg hatches.

It is interesting to note that this bird from a treeless land avoids or ignores trees when it migrates southward. The snowy owl is much more likely to perch on a mound, a cornstack, a post, the roof of an outbuilding, or a fisherman's shack. From such a vantage point it looks keenly about, equally ready to overtake a rabbit or a rat, or to scoop a wounded duck from the water.

Each winter a few snowy owls fly south to the northern United States, where they are most often seen in the vicinity of lakes or perched on a dune near the ocean. Some snowy owls are nearly pure white; these are the old males. The young and the females are barred with brownish gray. Although these arctic visitors are seldom harmful to game or poultry, they are often shot in large numbers, particularly when, as occasionally happens, the supply of lem-

Young Great Horned Owl

mings and hares in the Arctic is low and many of the owls are forced south by hunger. Naturalists are now seeking to protect this picturesque bird, which all too often ends up in a taxidermist's shop.

Another owl of the far north is the hawk owl, so called because it has a long tail and short wings like a sharp-shinned or Cooper's hawk, and like those species it hunts skillfully through brushy ground cover. It nests in tree cavities throughout the northernmost wooded country of America and Europe, as close to polar regions as northwestern Alaska, and visits the northerly parts of the United States only in winter. It is a daylight hunter, tackling anything from a hare or ptarmigan down to insects. Despite its hawklike habits, it retains the advantage of an owl's noiseless flight.

The sparrow-sized elf owl is the tiniest member of the family. It is nocturnal and spends the day in the same sort of place in which it nests, usually a woodpecker hole in a giant cactus. Insects appear to make up most of the elf owl's diet, but it is also ready for mice and other small mammals.

The owls so far discussed breed in barns, tree cavities, old nests of other birds, or on the ground. To find the home of the burrowing owl (Plates 26, 27) it is necessary to dig beneath the ground. In North America there are two races, the western and the Florida; others inhabit South America. Open country seems to be its main requirement, for the burrowing owl is everywhere a grassland bird. It is a fidgety, jerky, bobbing, perpetually curtsying, long-legged, thoroughly terrestrial-looking creature; a human intruder is likely to see it sitting on the mound above its burrow, glaring with blazing yellow eyes which somehow fail to have a fierce or threatening aspect.

The burrows may sometimes be scratched out by the owls, but they are more often old prairie dog or badger holes. In some cases the nest may be as much as ten feet from the entrance. Burrowing owls are, or were, most numerous in the once populous colonies of prairie dogs. Their presence in such places gave rise to fabulous stories about a Utopian association of owls, "dogs," badgers, and rattlesnakes. In fact, many a cowboy will still stake his honor on the truth of this tale!

All North American owls, except the barn owl and the barred owl, have yellow or orange eyes. The rich brown eyes of the barred owl lend a bland and friendly expression to its disk-shaped or spectacled and earless face. Although its feet are relatively weak, and fitted for catching mice rather than skunks, any suggestion that it has a gentle disposition would be misleading. From man's point of view, the barred owl, like most other owls, has generally useful feeding habits. Nevertheless, on several occasions the writers have heard at night the dying squeak of a bird picked off its perch in a forest of the Carolina Low Country and have been quite sure that the silent marauder was a barred owl. The barred owl might almost be called cannibalistic as well as predaceous, because the skeletal remains of several kinds of smaller owls have frequently been recovered from its pellets. But this cannibal has been known in turn to fall a victim to the great horned owl.

Preferring different kinds of country, the great horned owl and the barred owl are rarely found in the same forest. The barred owl is more common in luxuriant lowland

90

Richardson's Owl with Mouse

and deciduous river forest than in the upland. It seems remarkably tame, perhaps because its eyes are best adapted for minimum light intensities and it is therefore dazzled by bright daylight. Controlled experiments have shown that it can see well under light intensities of considerably less than one-tenth of what man requires for vision. The burrowing owl, a day-flying species, possesses, on the other hand, only about the same ability as man to see in weak light. Other experiments indicate that the ears of owls are vastly more sensitive than man's. When blindfolded and placed in a room, they can, guided only by hearing, catch mice that are running around on the floor. Why the ear openings of owls are apt to be asymmetrical—larger on one side of the head than on the other—is still not known.

The barred owl nests chiefly in hollow trees but has been known to make shift in an old hawk's nest. It has a considerable vocabulary of chuckles and grunts, but its telltale call is a series of eight sonorous, booming hoots, in groups of four, which carry a long distance. Barred owls range over most of the forests of North America east of the Rocky Mountains. Farther west their place is taken by a close relative, the spotted owl, a rare bird of similar habits.

Band-tailed Pigeon

Known to most Americans only because of southward winter flights, undertaken when normal food resources temporarily fail it, is the great gray or Lapp owl. Its range is the circumpolar coniferous forest, which means that it is found in Eurasia as well as North America. In the United States it breeds at only a few places south of the Canadian border; naturalists a few years ago made much of the fact that a pair was found nesting in the mountains near Yosemite Park in California.

The great gray (Plate 30) looks bigger than the great horned owl, though this impression is mainly the result of its remarkably long and loose plumage. It travels abroad by day in the far north—as it must do in lands close to the midnight sun—where it is said to prey mostly upon rabbits and to breed in the tree nests of other large birds. Little is yet known with certainty about its life history.

The long-eared (Plate 29) and the short-eared owls (Plate 30)—both terms referring to the relative size of the so-called ear tufts —belong to another group. The long-eared is a tree-nester, generally the beneficiary of a home built the previous year by a crow. It sticks to dense timber, especially evergreens, very carefully hides throughout the day, and sallies forth to catch mice—and little else—at night. Even after being located, it may be hard to see because, with closed eyes and compressed feathers, it can easily pass for a snapped-off branch. The best way to discover its hiding place is to search the ground for pellets in a copse of pines or cedars. The long-eared owl is not given to vocalizing as much as many other owls, though it becomes highly conversational during courtship and the rearing of the young.

The short-eared owl complements the long-eared in that it is a marsh and grassland bird, sleeping and nesting on the ground. Its total range is great, but its actual presence is limited to scattered, suitable localities. It is one of the Northern Hemisphere birds which has also penetrated South America as far as the grasslands of the remote Falkland Islands. The short-eared owl hunts both by day and by night, its main purpose in life being the capture of mice. Except at close range, it looks like a roundhead, the slender, closely spaced ear tufts hardly projecting as high as the crown of the head.

The little roundheaded saw-whet owl (Plate 37), an exclusively North American species, is known to most observers only as an irregular winter invader. When the saw-whets come, they often do so in force. The writers once flushed a dozen, one at a time, from the dense shelter of a red cedar tree. On another occasion a single errant bird slept the whole day through on a window grating of the American Museum of Natural History in the heart of New York City. Before departing, it dropped a single pellet which contained the remains of deer mice and insects.

The note of the saw-whet has a rasping character, resembling the sound made when a large-toothed saw is being filed; hence the name. It lives in woodpecker holes and flies with the swift wingbeat of a woodcock. It nests in the North in a hollow stub or even in a birdhouse. Richardson's owl is a slightly larger northern cousin of the sawwhet.

Pigeons and Doves   5

This group of birds is represented in the United States by only a few species, nine to be exact, of which four (including the extinct passenger pigeon) were native to the area east of the Mississippi. Few birds are better known than pigeons. One species, the rock pigeon of the Old World, was domesticated before the Christian era and is familiar to everyone. In America this pigeon lives in a semiwild condition both on city streets and in the country, where it nests in barns and seeks its food in grainfields.

Of the wild pigeons of North America, the most renowned was the passenger pi-

Poor-will

Chuck-will's-widow

geon, now totally extinct. The last free individual of this species was recorded in 1907; in captivity it survived for another decade. The story of the ruthless slaughter of this bird has been told so often that it need not be repeated here. Now that it is gone, the only member of its family that enjoys a wide distribution in the United States is the mourning dove (Plate 39). It is not so beautiful as the passenger pigeon, nor does it consort in spectacular migratory flocks, yet the mourning dove is so generally distributed in every state of the Union, as well as in Mexico and Canada, that some think it outnumbers all other birds in North America. Probably this species thrives because of its ability to live in almost all types of country except dense forest.

The mourning dove flies rapidly. Its flesh is excellent for human consumption. Dove shooting has become popular, especially in

the South, and conservation bureaus are paying increased attention to the protection and management of these birds. The mournful cooing of this dove, from which it receives its name, is still heard in most parts of America.

The little ground dove is so small that it is not hunted. It is an unwary creature and often walks about underfoot with utter unconcern. It is casual, too, in its nesting, and in Florida sometimes lays its eggs in a slight depression in short grass, where the parents and later the young are at the mercy of any predator that chances to pass. Elsewhere, as in Bermuda, it sometimes nests in shrubs. The ground dove is a southern species and is not to be expected north of Mason and Dixon's line.

In the towns and haciendas of the arid Southwest and in Mexico, the Inca dove (Plate 40) is ever present. Of retiring habits, it is easily overlooked, but its ceaselessly repeated two-syllable call, *no hope*, echoes through the hot, dry atmosphere. Like the ground dove in appearance, the Inca is a bit longer and slimmer and has white in the tail.

The band-tailed pigeon is a large, handsome species of the evergreen forests of western North America, from British Columbia to Central America. Its sonorous cooing or hooting is well known to those who visit these areas. In winter it sometimes comes down into the valleys of California to feed and is then hunted by the ranchers.

Several other pigeons and doves barely cross the southern borders of the United States but are common in Mexico. The white-winged dove (Plate 38) resembles the mourning dove but is stockier in build and has a less pointed tail. Both species can be found nesting in the cholla cactus of southern Arizona. The white-fronted dove and the red-billed pigeon enter the United States only in the Rio Grande Valley of southern Texas. Even there the clearing away of mesquite thickets has led to a decrease in numbers, but they are still common south of the border. The only other native species that requires mention is the white-crowned pigeon, a bird of the West Indies which occurs more or less regularly in the small islands or keys to the south of Florida.

A number of exotic species of doves have been introduced into the United States at one time or another. Aside from the domestic pigeon, or rock dove, the only ones that have become established are the Chinese spotted dove and the ringed turtle dove—and these two only in southern California.

Chimney Swift with Nest and Young

Cuckoos 6

The European cuckoo is famous for its voice—it is imitated by the cuckoo clock—and also because it lays its eggs in the nests of other birds, giving to the latter the task of hatching and caring for its young. The two common American species, the yellow-billed cuckoo (Plate 41) and the black-billed cuckoo (Plate 42), do not share this brood parasitism, as it is called. They build flimsy nests, hardly strong enough to hold the three or four unspotted, pale blue eggs that comprise a clutch or setting. Often the eggs can be seen from beneath the nest, as through a lattice. The newly hatched cuckoos are rather bizarre-looking creatures, bedecked with long, bristlelike feathers.

The yellow-billed and black-billed cuckoos are graceful birds, the length of a robin but much more slender. The yellow-billed can be distinguished from the black-billed not so much by the color of the bill as by its rufous-tinged wing feathers and its white-tipped tail. Both species subsist entirely upon insects and are among the few birds that are partial to hairy caterpillars. Hence they are highly migratory. The call notes are somewhat like those of the European cuckoo in quality, though not in pattern. A third species, the mangrove cuckoo, is found in the United States only in the coastal mangroves of southern Florida, but beyond the borders, in Mexico and the West Indies, it often lives in brush at some distance from the coast.

In the deserts of the Southwest, one of the most familiar birds is the road-runner (Plate 43)—America's only representative of a group known as ground cuckoos. It is a long-legged, long-tailed bird that dashes with great swiftness beneath the desert brush in pursuit of small snakes, lizards, and even, it is said, baby quail! A whole body of folklore has grown up about this bird, which is affectionately known to the Mexicans as *paisano*—"countryman." The road-runner is capable of flying for short distances. It shields its nest in a cactus or a mesquite bush.

The smooth-billed ani, a peculiar West Indian cuckoo, has established a small colony near the village of Homestead, Florida. It is a slender black bird, about a foot long, with a long, floppy tail. The bill is high and arched. Anis often walk and flutter about the feet of cattle to secure insects disturbed by the grazing animals.

(Continued on page 113)

73
Alder Flycatcher. Named after the shrub in which it nests. One of several flycatchers difficult to tell apart except by their songs.

96

74
Western Flycatcher. Shade-loving bird of the Rocky Mountains.

75
Mexican Crested Flycatcher. A bird of the southwestern deserts, it prefers nesting in old woodpecker holes in a giant cactus.

76

Least Flycatcher. Vocal little bird found on eastern tree-shaded streets. It sings its other name, "Che-bec."

77

Vermilion Flycatcher. Most brilliant member of its family. The male will flutter about for minutes at a time, displaying his colorful feathers to attract a mate.

78

Wright's Flycatcher. Found in the West in regions of thin woods or sagebrush.

79
*Olive-sided Flycatcher.
Common in the northern woods and in
mountain forests. Its lusty whistled
"Quick, three beers!" coming from a
treetop, identifies it.*

80

Scissor-tailed Flycatcher. One of the most striking of all our birds. In summer it is common in many parts of the Southwest.

Yellow-bellied Flycatcher. Difficult to identify, except in the spring when, as it migrates north, it can be told by its yellow underparts.

81

82

Horned Lark. The only true lark found in the New World.

83

Purple Martin. Its love of man-made dwellings dates from the days when the Indians hung up nesting gourds.

84

Cliff Swallow. A clever mason.

85

Bank Swallow. A bird of nearly world-wide distribution. Nests in holes in banks.

86 *Barn Swallow. Most familiar of all its family and most intimately associated with man. The sturdy nest, made of mud and grass, is lined with chicken feathers.*

87

Scrub Jay. So called because it lives in brush or "scrub."

88

*Scrub Jay. Widespread in
the Southwest, where it is
known as Woodhouse's jay;
in the East it lives only
in Florida.*

89

Blue Jay. Big, brilliantly colored, and vocal, this is the best-known jay throughout the eastern two-thirds of North America.

Pinyon Jay. A noisy, gregarious bird that lives among the pinyons and feeds on their nuts. It walks and flies like a crow, but looks like and is a jay.

90

91 *Florida Jay. Another race of the scrub jay, but usually tamer than the others.*

92

Steller's Jay. Blue jay of the West.

93

Yellow-billed Magpie. Found only in the foothills of central California. It nests in colonies.

94

Clark's Nutcracker. A bold and handsome mountain bird which has become a tourist attraction in the Rockies.

95

American Crow. Sly and alert, it survives even in areas where every effort is made to kill it off. In winter thousands often gather nightly to roost together.

96

Black-capped Chickadee. It braves the coldest storms.

97

*Brown-capped or Acadian
Chickadee. Cousin of the
black-cap, but brown-headed.
Inhabits evergreen forests
as far north as trees grow.*

Dipper
by Michael Warren

The dipper is a perching bird that has adapted to a life on the fast-flowing rivers and streams of the uplands in the west and north of the British Isles. It feeds on aquatic insects and other invertebrates. To catch its food it swims on and below the surface and it will even walk beneath the surface on the bed of a stream. The dipper breeds on the RSPB reserves at Coombes Valley in Staffordshire and the Dinas and Gwenffrwd in Carmarthenshire.

Birds are a national heritage and need your protection

This card is published by The Royal Society for the Protection of Birds, The Lodge, Sandy, Bedfordshire, from a specially commissioned picture, and the proceeds from its sale help in the work of bird protection.

98

*White-breasted Nuthatch. Sometimes called,
for obvious reasons, "devil-downhead."*

99

*Verdin. Found in the
mesquite thickets of
the Southwest, it
attracts attention by
its incessant chirping.*

100

*Dipper or Water Ouzel. Living
close to mountain torrents,
it plunges into the water and
walks along the bottom in
search of insects.*

101

Plain or Gray Titmouse. This western representative of the titmouse group is a rather shy and inconspicuous dweller in brush and open woodland.

102

Tufted Titmouse. It lives in the eastern United States, except the extreme north, and often nests in birdhouses.

103

Western Blue-gray Gnatcatcher. A tiny but pugnacious bird. It adorns and camouflages its nest with lichens.

104

Eastern Blue-gray Gnatcatcher. Its lichen-covered nest, seen here, is sometimes set high in a tree.

105

Long-billed Marsh Wren. Loud-voiced and energetic, it dwells in reeds and builds dummy nests in addition to the one occupied by the family.

106

Cactus Wren. The largest American wren. It builds its almost impregnable home in the core of a cactus.

107

*Carolina Wren. It is nonmigratory,
managing to survive as far
north as southern New York.*

108

*Canyon Wren. A crevice- or cave-dweller
of the Southwest; generally considered
the finest singer in its family.*

109

*House Wren. Pampered and
abundant as a result of free housing
provided by man. It is quick to
scold anyone approaching its nest.*

Goatsuckers 7

These eerie birds, more often heard than seen, have a wide distribution. Since they all feed upon flying insects, those of the northern latitudes are highly migratory, some of them crossing the equatorial regions to winter in the temperate belt of the Southern Hemisphere.

Goatsuckers are "all mouth and no bill." For this reason the Romans had a legend that the European nightjar was a surreptitious *capri mulgus* or milker of goats. Such is the origin of both the scientific and popular names of the family. Goatsuckers are active mostly at night or in the twilight hours of morning and evening, although bands of nighthawks often migrate by day and occasionally form impressive whirling circles over places where the air is thick with insects.

One of the largest North American goatsuckers is the chuck-will's-widow of the southeastern United States. It is rare north of Virginia and southern Indiana. Its nocturnal call, musical yet mysterious at close range, is in general similar to that of the whip-poor-will but has one extra syllable. The whip-poor-will, however, avoids the close vicinity of water—for reasons yet unknown — whereas the chuck-will's-widow freely hides and sings at the very brink of ponds, rivers, or salt lagoons. The authors have heard it make the night ring within a few feet of tidal channels among the sea islands of the Southern Atlantic coast. Like that of most goatsuckers, its plumage presents a mottled pattern of blending browns, grays, and whites, which makes it nearly invisible when it is at rest on the ground.

The persistent call of the whip-poor-will (Plate 44), repeated scores or even hundreds of times, is a familiar night sound. A whistled imitation will lure the birds, particularly in the season of mating and of appropriation of nesting territories. With such whistling the authors have frequently had three or four, presumably males, fluttering belligerently around them in the dusk. The English name is a good rendering of the notes, as was the Algonquin Indian name, Wagulí. But the Gaspé farmers in Quebec interpret the call as *cuir pourri* (rotten leather). When these words are repeated with the proper French roll, they reproduce the sound made by this bird even better than does the name whip-poor-will.

The birds arrive from the South and the West Indies before the end of April and remain until frost. They nest early, laying two protectively colored eggs on the brown litter of the forest floor. When flushed, they fly off in ghostly silence, although they are also apt to put on an elaborate broken-wing performance which has the effect of turning one's attention from the eggs. The plumage of the birds, both adults and young, also provides good camouflage and is remarkably beautiful in its mingling of rich brown, buff, and near-gold. When they crouch on a limb—always lengthwise rather than crosswise, like all other members of the family—it is almost impossible for the eye to spot them.

Like many other goatsuckers, the whip-

Acorn Woodpecker

poor-will has long rictal bristles behind the diminutive bill. These help make a collecting net of the capacious mouth which, when open, fairly splits the head in half.

The poor-will is a small goatsucker of southwestern United States and adjacent parts of Mexico. It is easily recognized by its two-syllable call. One night in Arizona the authors came on one performing in the middle of a dusty road; the car was stopped with the bird in the full glare of the headlights, but it continued to call with undiminished vigor.

For many years there have been occasional reports of poor-wills picked up during the winter in a semitorpid condition. It was generally assumed that such individuals were only temporarily numbed by low temperatures. Recently Edmund C. Jaeger proved that the poor-will sometimes remains in such a condition for a period of two or three months during the cold season. At such times its body temperature is greatly depressed—from a normal of 100 degrees Fahrenheit to about 66 degrees—and respiration is proportionately slowed. In other words, the poor-will hibernates; it is the only bird known to do so. It is still not known whether all poor-wills from the northern parts of their range hibernate, or whether some of them migrate. Professor Jaeger found that one individual returned for two successive winters to sleep in the same rock cranny. One race of this bird has feathers tipped with white and is known as the frosted poor-will.

The nighthawk is a bird of about a dozen subspecies scattered throughout North and Central America. Generally speaking, it inhabits more open country than the whip-poor-will. Even the eastern nighthawk, which is at home in thin woodlands, also nests in many bare places, such as on the flat, tarred and pebbled roofs of city houses. Persons observant of birds are quick to hear its penetrating calls, which sound like *beeing,* coming from high in the air above the clamor of busy streets. Seen from below it appears as a long-winged rakish bird with white wing spots.

In western parts of the continent some races of the nighthawk live in desert areas, and their booming as they make breathless dives, with the wind whistling through their primary feathers, is as familiar to campers as the howling of coyotes. Like other goatsuckers, a nighthawk scurries about in swift and dexterous flight, quickly cramming its mouth and throat with insects. Mosquito hawk is another appropriate common name for it; five hundred mosquitoes have actually been counted in the throat and stomach of a single bird.

At times of fancied danger, young nighthawks keep their bright eyes tightly closed and are so well concealed by their resemblance to their surroundings that it is possible to step over them without seeing them. They grow extraordinarily fat from their insect diet. The few fledglings we have handled were actually heavier than their parents.

Swifts   8

Swifts are remarkably specialized for catapulting through the air at top speed in pursuit of flying insects. They fly with tremendous verve and dash and seem to be on the wing all day long. Hurtling along in groups of twos or threes, twittering loudly, they seem to fly for the sheer joy of it.

Swifts build their nests in caves or on the insides of hollow trees. Their saliva is very gluey and they use it to fasten nesting material together. The nest of the edible-nest swift of the Orient is composed solely of such hardened saliva. Melted down, it forms the bird's-nest soup of the Chinese. Swifts are often confused with swallows by the uninitiated, but the two are not closely related.

The chimney swift is found in the eastern United States, where it is a common summer bird. It formerly nested in hollow trees but now, as the name suggests, lives in chimneys. It also uses the inside walls of silos, barns, and old log cabins. The nest is built of dead twigs that the swift, pausing momentarily in flight, snaps off with its feet. The twigs are joined to each other and attached to the supporting surface by the gluelike saliva. In common with all other swifts, it lays white eggs. The young call for food noisily; when half grown they leave the scanty little nest platform and cling to the wall. Their tail feathers end in spiny tips, which enable them to cling to perpendicular surfaces. One or two unmated swifts often become affiliated with a nesting pair and spend the entire season cooperating more or less closely in the nesting activities. Such "assistants" may acquire mates the following year or they may again fill a secondary role as helpers at the nest.

The winter home of the chimney swift was long a mystery. In an effort to solve the enigma, thousands of them were captured by placing nets across the openings of chimneys during the migratory flocking season and were banded. In time a few of these bands were brought to a local official by Peruvian Indians; the latter had done a little swift-trapping of their own and thus discovered the winter home of the species. E. T. Gilliard, of the American Museum of Natural History, has reported seeing flocks of swifts roosting in a chimney in the city of Manaus, Brazil, indicating that even in the southern continent, human culture is leading to a change in the habits of these birds.

The white-throated swift of the West nests on the walls of rocky canyons. It is a little larger than the chimney swift, and its flight has the breath-taking velocity attained by some of the large tropical species.

The black swift, the largest American species ranges northward into the western United States as far as Colorado. It builds a little nest on a ledge and lays only a single egg. Like many other swifts, it prefers a home in the vicinity of a waterfall. Often it flies directly through the spray to nest in crannies behind the falls. After the young hatch, they are fed only once or twice a day by their parents, who may be away all day long on foraging flights.

Hummingbirds 9

Hummingbirds are the smallest of birds and among the most brilliantly colored. The color of male hummers is usually brightest on the throat or gorget, an area displayed during dazzling courtship flights. In some species the tail or wing feathers are stiffened and produce whistling notes as the birds zoom through the air before their mates. Even in normal flight the wings make the humming noise for which these birds were named. The wings are attached to the shoulders by joints that permit a rotary motion almost as free as that of a propeller. Analysis of high-speed photographs of the ruby-throated hummingbird reveals that the number of wing beats varies from 50 to 75 per second. This is far greater than that found in any other group of birds, and permits hummingbirds to hover motionless while feeding, to fly backwards, or to dash ahead at full speed. The bird's endurance, too, is very great, and it is commonly asserted that the ruby-throat migrates nonstop across the Gulf of Mexico.

East of the Mississippi River there is only one hummingbird, the familiar ruby-throat. In the West three or four species are of general distribution, one of which, the rufous hummingbird (Plate 52) reaches Alaska. Several additional species cross the southern borders of Arizona and Texas. In South America there are literally hundreds of kinds of hummers. Despite the endless variety of their colors and ornamental plumes, the habits of all of them are similar. They feed upon nectar, tiny insects, and spiders, and prefer red blossoms, especially those with a long flower tube or corolla. Into such flowers the hovering hummer thrusts its long thin bill and through its long tongue, which is a tiny, hollow tube, the nectar ascends by capillary attraction.

The tip of the tongue is frayed out into a little brush with which insects are whisked into the mouth. Because of their fondness for nectar, hummingbirds love sweetened water and quickly learn to feed from glass tubes containing it. Charles Cordier, bird collector for the New York Zoological Park, has given much attention to the care of hummingbirds and has published a dietary formula for keeping them in captivity. He has also brought from South America species never before exhibited; most of these were captured by natives who stun the birds with pellets of clay shot through a blow gun.

The nests of hummingbirds are as small and attractive as the birds themselves. They are usually placed in a crotch of a bush or on a horizontal limb and are often camouflaged with bits of lichen attached by spider web. Two tiny white eggs are laid. The young, black and ugly when hatched, grow rapidly. Their mother inserts her bill into the throat of the babies and literally pumps them full of food. As a rule the male takes no part in building the nest, incubating the eggs, or caring for the young. In the black-chinned hummingbird (Plates 45, 47) of the Southwest the female sometimes raises brood after brood, beginning a second nest and clutch of eggs while she is still feeding the first brood.

The voice of the hummingbird is no more than a series of squeaks or twitters, and is uttered to express displeasure. Hummingbirds are very pugnacious and expel larger birds from their territories with a buzzing, whirlwind attack that leaves their foes bewildered. They do not spare members of their own species. The males protect their favorite display grounds with great fervor and in the winter stake out feeding territories which they also defend vigorously.

Many of the early explorers of North America, including Champlain, noted the hummingbird in their journals, for none of the Old World species familiar to the pioneers in any way resembled it. Even to this day countryfolk sometimes wonder whether the hummer is really a bird. Others make the opposite error and conclude that the sphinx moths which they see hovering over flowers at dusk are hummingbirds. Most of the species of western hummingbirds seem almost indistinguishable from one another when in flight, and only those proficient in bird study can hope to identify them, especially the plainly colored females and the immature birds. Once their habits and seasons are learned, identification becomes simpler. Some of them can actually be recognized by the pitch of the humming sound produced in flight; the wings of the broad-tailed hummingbird (Plate 46), for instance, produce a shrill buzzing, unlike that of any other kind.

The largest hummers to enter the limits of the United States are the blue-throated and the Rivoli's (Plate 49) but both are rare and occur only near the Mexican border. Of the tiny Costa's hummingbird (Plate 51), another southwestern species, the eminent author of *The Life Histories of North American Birds*, A. C. Bent, has written: "The gorgeous glowing colors of its brilliant helmet adorn, in the male, the top of the head, the throat, and the elongated feathers on the sides of the gorget; the burnished metallic violet of these feathers changes in certain lights to royal purple, magenta, blue, or even green." Anna's hum-

mingbird of California (Plate 48) has a remarkable courtship flight. Mounting high in the air, it plunges vertically at great speed. As it pulls out of this power dive, the air sets the tail quills in vibration—or so it is thought—and a loud chirping note is produced. The broad-billed hummingbird (Plate 50) is another of the Mexican species that crosses the border into southern Arizona. Its flight is so swift that one writer has compared the sound made by its wings to the whine of a rifle bullet.

Trogons and Kingfishers   10

The coppery-tailed trogon (Plate 54) is the northern pioneer of a family of colorful tropical birds. It crosses the American borders nowhere except in southern Texas and Arizona and only in small numbers. The first nest to be discovered in the United States was found by Dr. Arthur A. Allen in a canyon of the Santa Rita Mountains, but the birds are said to have since disappeared from that locality.

Trogons nest in holes in trees. The three or four eggs are white; both sexes incubate. Of sedate habits, they are usually seen only when they take wing or utter their rather low-pitched notes. The resplendent quetzal, national bird of Guatemala, and by some considered the most beautiful bird in the world, is a relative of the coppery-tailed trogon.

The belted kingfisher (Plate 53) is a widespread North American bird. True, it is restricted to the vicinity of water, but any body of water will do. The authors have found it at home on a beaver pond in the remote Raft River Mountains of Utah, north of the Great Salt Desert, and have also watched it seek a roost in the rafters below a bridge across a tidal creek on a parkway in Brooklyn.

The kingfisher is not easily overlooked—its huge head with bill to match, and its belligerent rattling cry see to that. Since it is sometimes a pest at fish hatcheries—which really tempt it irresistably—it might behoove the kingfisher to be a bit more retiring, but it is alert and wary and survives all the persecution directed its way. Most of the animus felt by fishermen is undeserved, for under normal conditions this bird feeds chiefly on the "weed" fish which compete with game fish for food.

When hungry the kingfisher flies over shallow water until it spots a school of small fish. Then it hovers in the air, selects a victim, and plunges into the water after its prey, often from as great a height as thirty feet. The kingfisher then carries the fish to a convenient perch, pounds it once or twice on a limb to quiet it, and swallows it head first.

At pairing time the kingfishers dig a deep tunnel into the vertical bank of a stream or into the side of a gravel pit. They raise a large family—six or eight young. By the time the latter leave home, the nest chamber is littered with the bones of the fish consumed by the family.

Woodpeckers are preeminently adapted for climbing on tree trunks in search of insects. Their claws are sharp and curved and their tail feathers pointed and stiff at the ends to provide a prop against the bark. The central pair of tail feathers molts last (not first as in most other birds) and only after the other new tail feathers are well grown. In this way the tail remains useful at all times; without it the bird could not cling to the tree. The bill is shaped like a chisel —and serves as one—and the skull is unusually thick. The woodpecker can bang away with might and main for hours with no signs of weariness, and doubtless without "seeing stars"! Some of the larger species dig nesting holes a foot or more deep in the heart of live trees.

The tongue of the woodpecker is very long and can be pushed out for a surprising distance—usually more than the length of the bird's head. The hyoid or tongue bones extend back on the side of the lower jaws and curve over the top of the skull, ending in the vicinity of the eye sockets! These long springlike bones allow the tongue to be flicked in and out. Dr. Southgate Hoyt took pictures showing that the tongue of the pileated woodpecker can be extended through the mesh of a wire screen and then bent at right angles. The action is so rapid as to appear to be a blur. The woodpecker's tongue is pointed and has barbs like fish-hooks near its tip; it serves as an effective spear for extracting soft grubs.

Woodpeckers are not songbirds; instead they produce a rolling drumbeat by striking the bill rapidly against a dry, resonant limb. This drumming announces that the woodpecker is ready to welcome a mate or to give combat to trespassers. Woodpeckers also have a variety of vocal notes, most of which are loud and not very melodious.

The most familiar American woodpecker is the little black-and-white downy (Plate 65), which is to be seen even around city parks. It has a nasal *peent* of alarm and a sharp, whinnying cry. Like most other woodpeckers it can dig out hidden insects in the winter, and so does not need to migrate. The hairy woodpecker, a larger cousin of the downy, prefers to live in forests rather than in shade trees and orchards. The downy and hairy woodpeckers are both named for the short, almost woolly, feathers which conceal their nostrils. Such protection against frost is found in many birds of the north. The little ladder-backed or cactus woodpecker (Plate 56) of the deserts of the Southwest is much like a downy, even though it lives in such an utterly different environment.

Also well known is the flicker (Plate 64). Among its many local names are high-hole and golden-winged woodpecker. Its bill is not so sharp and chisel-shaped as that of other woodpeckers, and it is less of a wood-driller. The flicker eats many ants and spends much time on the ground in search of them. Its eggs, like those of all woodpeckers, are glossy white. In the West the resident species is the red-shafted flicker (Plate 66), while in the Southwest the so-called gilded flicker holds forth among the giant cacti of the desert. Although a large, stocky bird, the flicker is sometimes evicted from its nest burrow by the pugnacious starling. The flicker may not succeed in raising a family until the nesting season of the starling is over and it is at last left in peace.

Another woodpecker of interesting habits is the sapsucker (Plate 62). In the spring it drills rows of holes in apple trees to which it returns from time to time to drink the sap that has oozed out. This weakens the tree, but the sapsucker is rarely numerous enough to cause serious damage. It also eats large numbers of insects. Sapsuckers vary considerably in color in different parts of the United States, but they may all be recognized at a glance by the conspicuous white line on the shoulder. One species, the yellow-bellied sapsucker, ranges across the continent; another, the Williamson's sapsucker, resides only in the western mountains. Sapsuckers sometimes produce a tremendous din by drumming on tin signs, a habit which the flicker shares.

The red-headed woodpecker (Plate 57) is commonest in the Middle West and South, but also occurs in scattered localities in the East. It prefers shade trees and telephone poles along public roads, and as a result is often killed by automobiles. On a sunny day, the red-head will fly out from a convenient telephone pole in pursuit of flying insects. It supplements its diet with ripe berries, and at times even raids the nest of other hole-dwelling birds. Apparently it does not like competitors. Young woodpeckers, when well grown, are very noisy; a nestful of red-headed woodpeckers produces a noise like an overtaxed steam boiler.

Lewis's woodpecker (Plate 59), named for one of the leaders of the Lewis and Clark Expedition, is black, gray, and salmon-red. Its broad wings give it a jaylike appearance. More or less closely related to the red-head and the Lewis's woodpecker are three species, the red-bellied woodpecker (Plate 58) in the Southeast, the golden-fronted woodpecker (Plate 55) of Texas and Mexico, and the Gila woodpecker (Plate 61) of Arizona. These birds all have a loud and trilling cry. Another member of this group is the species variously called the California woodpecker, the ant-eating woodpecker, and the acorn woodpecker (Plate 63). The name of the last derives from the bird's habit of drilling rows of holes in a tree, in each of which it tucks an acorn.

The most spectacular of American woodpeckers are the pileated (Plate 60) and the ivory-billed. Both have long, pointed crests which in the male are red. The ivory-bill, greatest of American woodpeckers, is now on the very brink of extinction. Only in Florida are a few pairs known to survive. Closely related ivory-bills are found in Cuba and in western Mexico. They, too, are dangerously reduced in numbers.

The pileated woodpecker, or logcock, as it is sometimes called, is not so exacting in its requirements as the ivory-bill, and has learned to live in second-growth woods. With the abandonment of thousands of acres of submarginal farmland, the pileated has moved into these second-growth forests and is now commoner than it was a generation ago. It prefers as food the carpenter ants, which enter trees from the ground and eat away the heartwood. To reach the ants, this woodpecker labors mightily; the pile of chips below a tree where it has been digging often fills a bushel basket. The heavy blows of its bill are audible for some distance. The nest chamber is cut into the heart of a live tree and is a foot or more in depth. Its entrance is usually somewhat rectangular in shape, rather than round as in the nests of other woodpeckers. Both parents aid in incubating the eggs and in caring for the young. Curiously enough, in many woodpeckers the female gradually loses interest in her family, even before the young are ready to leave the nest, and the male shoulders the entire task of feeding them.

The pileated woodpecker stays in the far north throughout the winter. At that season each individual digs a hole in a tree to which it retires for protection during the night. This habit, necessary for conserving body heat and vigor during the long cold nights, is shared by many birds, particularly the smaller ones, that winter in the North.

Flycatchers 12

The American flycatchers comprise an exclusively New World family. The great center of their abundance is in Central and South America, the thirty species of temperate North America representing a sort of overflow from the tropical source.

The Old World flycatchers, including those of Europe, belong to quite a different family. Similar feeding habits seem, however, to have been accompanied by parallel development in the two groups. As a result, there are many resemblances of structure and appearance, such as a flattened bill, an upright, "square-shouldered" sitting posture, and a way of darting out in pursuit of prey and then returning to the same perch. American flycatchers are very important in the control of insects. This does not mean that they confine their diet to the kinds of insects that man calls "injurious," but rather that they help keep the entire insect population within normal bounds. Since the bulk of their food consists of flying insects, they are necessarily highly migratory, all species retreating southward to latitudes with an abundant winter insect population. The kingbirds and certain other kinds vary their diet, however, by eating small fruits, such as elderberries. Nearly all flycatchers are aggressive, particularly toward larger birds, the bold behavior of the kingbird being a byword among country-folk.

The eastern kingbird (Plate 67), which inhabits all but the extreme western and southwestern third of the United States, as well as much of southern Canada, derives its name equally from its demeanor and its partially concealed crown patch of red feathers. It is distinctly self-advertising, with a loud, cheerful, almost hysterical twitter. With great zest it pitches into crows, hawks, or even larger interlopers on its territory. Twice the authors have unwittingly, and very unwillingly, been a party to the death of kingbirds that dived headlong into a car they were driving. Apparently the vehicle had passed near a nest at about the time eggs were hatching, and the parent

bird had thought it an approaching enemy.

The home site of kingbirds is very frequently in orchard trees, well out toward the end of a high bough. When the nest is approached, the kingbirds sally out boldly in its defense and are easily recognized by their white breasts and white-tipped tail feathers.

The western or Arkansas kingbird (Plate 68), with its yellow underparts, is rather different from the eastern kingbird in appearance, but its habits are much the same. Its range virtually complements that of the eastern bird but it seems to be spreading eastward, and is not uncommonly found as an autumn straggler in states along the Atlantic seaboard.

The beautiful scissor-tailed flycatcher (Plate 80) is one of the continent's most striking birds. The streaming tail feathers are longer than the rest of the body. It is plain gray above, salmon-pink on the belly, pearly gray on the head, breast, and back, and it has a red crown patch and red side stripes. The scissor-tails are birds of the Great Plains, where one sometimes sees them just clearing the ground cover before swooping upward to a high perch in an isolated tree or on a telephone wire. During courtship, the male makes spectacular use of its long, flexible tail in aerial dances. The species shares all the pluck and pugnacity of the kingbirds.

The crested flycatcher brings us back into the realm of familiar eastern birds. This woodland species with a rufous tail and a rich, slightly husky call of remarkably low musical pitch, inhabits approximately the eastern half of the United States and adjacent parts of Canada. It somewhat resembles the yellow-breasted group of kingbirds but differs in its breeding habits, for it nests in cavities and will even accept man-made birdhouses if they are erected in suitable shade. Its food consists more of forest moths, caterpillars, and beetles than of flies, and it is also fond of sassafras fruits and various berries.

The crested flycatcher sometimes incorporates the cast-off dry skins of snakes in its big and ragged nest. It has been all too easy for people to assume that the birds make deliberate use of the snake skin as a protective "frightener." Now that snakes are relatively rare and cellophane wrappers all too common, it has become evident that the flycatcher has no more interest in one than the other! It simply has a liking for such crinkly material. The Mexican crested flycatcher (Plate 75) is a closely related southwestern species.

Especially well known around human habitations and widely distributed in eastern North America is the phoebe (Plate 70). The earliest spring arrival among flycatchers, it sometimes appears before the last snow flurries and, if insects have been thoroughly inhibited by cold, ekes out its diet with such clinging fruits and berries as those of poison ivy. The phoebe takes its name, of course, from its insistent and very emphatic call. Its constant tail-wagging is equally characteristic. Unlike most of its relatives, it winters in the temperate zone, chiefly in the southern part of the United States. Nowadays its nest is more likely to be in a man-made structure than elsewhere —on the beam of a porch or under a bridge, for phoebes are fond of the vicinity of water. Perhaps the oldest North American

experiment in bird-banding was carried through when Audubon encircled the leg of a phoebe with a silver wire and established the fact that the marked bird came back to the same nest site the following spring.

A western cousin is the black phoebe (Plate 71), which is confined to the Pacific Coast and the slopes of the Sierra Nevadas from Oregon southward into Mexico. Of more northern range, reaching to Alaska and spreading eastward to the corn belt of the central United States, is Say's phoebe (Plate 69), which can be told by its rust-colored belly. The black and Say's phoebes have habits similar to those of the eastern bird.

A group of flycatchers which includes a number of diminutive species of the genus *Empidonax* presents endless difficulties of identification because of the close resemblances among them. They can be readily spotted through their call notes, distinctive and characteristic, but if encountered on southward migration, when they are silent, the task of identification becomes all but hopeless. In the case of several of these flycatchers many experts agree that museum specimens are even more difficult to identify than the living birds, which can at least "speak their names." Only one of them, the yellow-bellied flycatcher (Plate 81), may be readily singled out; its underparts, including the throat, are bright yellow. Of all American birds, it is one of the latest of spring migrants. Three others, the Acadian, alder, and least flycatchers, are almost dead ringers for one another. Roger Tory Peterson points out in his *Field Guide to the Birds* that the least (Plate 76) is the grayest, the Acadian greener, and the alder (Plate 73) browner, but these differences are rather subtle. Fortunately, when they can be heard, the calls tell the story, for the least flycatcher says *che-béc*, the alder *way-be-o*, and the Acadian *spit-chee*. Furthermore, the birds select more or less different types of nesting terrain and inhabit somewhat different climatic zones, the Acadian being the most southerly, the alder the most northerly, and the least a farm and orchard dweller in intermediate areas.

In the West the number of confusing species is even greater. In addition to the alder or Traill's flycatcher, whose range extends across the continent, one may encounter Wright's flycatcher (Plate 78) and Hammond's flycatcher. They are generally considered indistinguishable in the field, unless one hears and knows their song. The gray flycatcher, another western species, is also confusing, but Dr. A. R. Phillips has pointed out that it wags its tail like a phoebe, though less vigorously, whereas all other related species jerk the tail up and down. The gray flycatcher nests in winter-killed shrubbery among sagebrush, and usually within a foot or so of the ground. It also seeks mountain elevations as much as five thousand feet above the sea. Most other members of *Empidonax* prefer heavier cover, and only Wright's flycatcher goes higher up the mountains, even to the edge of the snow.

The western flycatcher (Plate 74), bearing the scientific name *difficilis*—appropriate for many members of the genus—is still another Rocky Mountain species of extensive north-south range (Alaska to Lower California). It is brighter yellow below than any of the other western species, thus differing from its congeners in the same manner that the yellow-bellied flycatcher does from those of eastern North America. Finally, the buff-breasted flycatcher is an *Empidonax* that crosses the southern border of the United States to breed only in the Mountain ranges of Arizona and New Mexico.

A recent exchange of ideas among experienced American ornithologists has brought out the following points of appearance and behavior that may help in the identification of such exasperating little birds as the members of *Empidonax*:

The least flycatcher has a terminally rounded tail, whereas that of the Acadian is very slightly notched. The yellow-bellied stays rather close to the ground for both feeding and nesting; the alder flycatcher, on the other hand, seeks higher levels. The least flycatcher has the most invariable song of them all. It is more like *tze-bék* or *te-hik* than the *che-béc* that has given the bird one of its common names. The song of the Acadian, however, can be readily confused with one of the alder flycatcher's vocal performances. In different parts of the continent, the song of the alder varies. It may well be that what is called the alder flycatcher actually comprises two slightly different and reproductively isolated populations, one of them a plains bird and the other an eastern woodland bird. It is in such kinds of diversification that the origin of races or subspecies is to be sought.

Among other representatives of the large flycatcher family are the wood pewees. American flycatchers are not typical songbirds, but the music of the eastern pewee's

124

well-known plaintive call almost lifts it into that category. The eastern pewee is a forest flycatcher, residing throughout eastern North America from Canada to Florida and westward to the limit of abundant tree growth in the Central states, or as far as the Dakotas and Kansas. It is a late breeder, a builder of a lichen-covered nest whose beauty is famous, and a bird of singular charm produced by a combination of quietness in behavior and a slightly melancholy sweetness in its notes. The western wood pewee (Plate 72), although similar in appearance to the eastern bird, is a distinct species, rather than a mere race. It lives between the Great Plains and the Pacific, all the way from Canada to Mexico. But it does not sing *pee-a-wee*, nor does it camouflage its nest with a covering of lichens.

The olive-sided flycatcher (Plate 79) is bigger than the pewees—almost the size of the kingbird. It is a dark, large-headed bird of markedly upright posture, a lover of evergreen woodlands and of high dead treetops. From such watchtowers it sallies forth to snap up insects. From the same perches it also fairly shouts its insistent telltale call, which has been likened to someone calling, "Quick, three beers!" It is a northern bird, except in higher elevations of mountain ranges, and in most parts of the United States we see it chiefly during its migrations to or from tropical America.

In a family of prevailing somber-plumaged birds, it is astonishing to find the dazzling vermilion flycatcher (Plate 77), which lives in the so-called desert country of the Southwest, between southern Texas and southeastern California. In this species, the female is plain and not unlike other un-distinguished flycatchers, whereas her mate has scarlet (rather than vermilion) on the crown of the crested head and the entire under surface of the body. The wings and tail are grayish brown.

The male vermilion flycatcher is a ball of fire in more than appearance, for it has an extraordinarily showy courtship and nuptial performance, its aerial dance being accompanied by a voluble tinkling song. It is also fearless, aggressive, and apparently fond of tackling prey nearly as big as itself. The authors have watched one perching on a tall cactus and by spasmodic struggles, painful to the observer, contriving gradually to crumple up and swallow an enormous dragonfly. No doubt the hard chitinous parts of such insects are later regurgitated, because it is known that many flycatchers eject pellets of indigestible material, just as owls disgorge the bones and fur of rodents. The vermilion flycatcher, despite its desert predilections, is fond of water, near which it usually builds a nest bound with cobwebs and decorated with lichens, thus rivaling that of the wood pewee.

The little beardless flycatcher of southernmost Arizona and the lower Rio Grande Valley in Texas is the smallest and dullest colored of the family. It is said to search for food rather in the manner of a warbler or a vireo and to vary its insect diet with small fruits. Its nest is also peculiar, being globular, with a side entrance, but its voice is that of a flycatcher—and powerful for so small a bird. The call has been transcribed as *yoop-yoop, yoop, eé-deedle-deé.*

The cotingas, a family of tropical American birds allied to the flycatchers, include

125

such spectacular and colorful creatures as the cock-of-the-rock and the umbrella bird. One member of this family, the rose-throated becard, extends as far north as the United States, barely reaching the border. It is of very sparse distribution in southern Arizona and Texas.

Larks 13

This family of songbirds is represented in North America by a single species, the horned lark (Plate 82), so called because two tufts of feathers project from its forehead. It is a bird of open grasslands, deserts, and tundra. As the eastern forests gave way before the ax, the horned lark followed. The expanses of sand and beach grass on Long Island are also to its liking, and it now nests within the city limits of New York.

Larks have a streaked coloration and are difficult to see when they crouch in the grass or sand. In Asia and Africa this agreement of coloration with background is such that where the soil of a region is black, the larks are often blackish, and where it is red, they are reddish. Thus the family provides a fine example of protective coloration.

Larks soar high in the air to pour forth their melodies. The skylark of Europe is justly celebrated for beautiful flight song; although the song of the American horned lark may not be so renowned, it is, none-

theless, an attractive tinkling melody and is given in fine weather at almost any season of the year.

The horned lark nests northward far into the Arctic, and the flocks that visit the United States in winter come from these polar breeding grounds. Commonly called shore larks because of their abundance along sandy coasts, they also find the wide expanses of airports to their liking. They live on the seeds of grass and weeds.

Swallows 14

Swallows are among the best known and best loved of songbirds. In America it is considered a good omen to have a colony of barn swallows on one's property; in Europe people have the same feeling about the house martin.

Swallows are preeminently birds of the air. With long pointed wings and streamlined bodies, they sweep about in pursuit of insects or glide low over a pond to scoop up, while in full flight, a sip of water. In the barn swallow (Plate 86), and to a lesser extent in some of the others, the tail is forked, which adds to the gracefulness of flight. The dependence of swallows upon flying insects means that these birds must depart for warmer climes at the beginning of cold weather. Their return is eagerly awaited for they are regarded as harbingers of spring.

Favorite songsters though they are, swallows are less accomplished in this respect than many other birds. Barn swallows are a possible exception, for on a cool May morning these birds, enjoying the first warm rays of the morning sun on the beam in an old barn, sometimes express their well-being by warbling softly to one another.

The cliff or eave swallow (Plate 84), a rather close relative of the barn swallow, also nests about barns, but fastens its flask-like mud nest on the outside of the building under the eaves, rather than on a beam inside. In the West the cliff swallow still builds its nest on cliffs along rivers. Colonies may comprise hundreds of nests, crowded together in dense clusters, each with a little spout through which the swallows enter and leave. These spouts permit the nests to be clustered together without interfering unduly with the privacy of each family.

In the South the purple martin (Plate 83) is a familiar bird near households. Hollow gourds were supplied for its nesting by the American Indians, and these or more elaborate martin houses are still erected for its convenience. It also nests in crannies about barns and under roof tiles. In the Southwest, where it occupies holes in the giant cactus, the martin retains its primitive nesting habits. The martin, like the cliff swallow, nests in colonies. In the North, English sparrows often take over martin houses, and perhaps for this reason the purple martin is rather local in distribution in the Northern states.

Another species that takes advantage of bird houses is the tree swallow. Steel-blue above, snow-white below, it is a handsome swallow. The nest is usually built in a hollow stump near a pond, but bird houses are very acceptable to it. In the far west the violet-green swallow, a related species, also nests in bird houses.

There are, in fact, only two North American members of the family that do not nest in bird houses or on buildings erected by man, the bank swallow (Plate 85) and the rough-winged swallow. They are similar in appearance, brown above, whitish below. The bank swallow has a well-defined brownish band across the chest, below the white throat; in the rough-wing the underparts are more uniform. Both of these swallows nest in burrows which they dig for themselves in vertical earthen banks, the excavation of the rough-wing usually being very shallow. The bank swallow nests in colonies, the rough-wing in scattered pairs. The rough-wing, which gets its name from the presence of tiny hooks on the forward edge of the wings, sometimes places its nest among the roots of an overturned tree or in drainage pipes emerging from banks or culverts.

Jays, Magpies, and Crows   15

Crows, ravens, magpies, nutcrackers, and jays—all members of one family—are among the largest of the so-called perching birds. Technically they belong to the songbird group although, to be sure, the croaking of ravens, the cawing of crows, and the screaming of jays are not fine music. Yet jays sometimes utter soft "whisper songs" as they sit contentedly sunning themselves in a sheltered bush, and even the somber raven utters far-carrying, mellow calls that have been compared to the sound of water pouring from the mouth of a jug. Unlike each other in appearance, the various members of the crow family are alike in being saucy, impudent birds, sly or bold as the occasion may require, and with thieving habits. All of them at times eat the eggs and young of birds, but they offset this by disposing of many harmful insects.

Jays

The blue jay (Plate 89) is *the* jay of eastern North America. It is a beautiful bird, especially when seen against a background of snow and pines, for like other members of the family it is, for the most part, nonmigratory. The call of the blue jay is a series of raucous screams: *jay, jay, jay*. Only slightly less familiar is its "pump-handle" note; and it is also adept at mimicking the harsh cries of the red-shouldered hawk. Although blue jays can be very secretive when nesting, at other seasons they consort in noisy bands. If such flocks chance upon a sleeping owl or a roving fox, they scream in delight and annoy the unfortunate victim until it flees. In the autumn blue jays feed upon acorns, beechnuts, and other mast. They hide away surplus nuts in crevices of bark or bury them beneath a few leaves on the ground. Many of these are never recovered, and jays share with gray squirrels

credit for having planted many of the historic white oak forests.

The Steller's jay (Plate 92), a western relative of the blue jay, was first seen by Georg Steller, a member of the Russian Expedition that discovered Alaska in 1741. In coloration this jay is less varied and beautiful than the eastern blue jay, but in habits and behavior it is much the same.

The pinyon jay (Plate 90), another western variety, inhabits rocky slopes covered by junipers and pinyon pines. Its liking for the sweet pinyon nuts, which are relished by Indians and indeed by all who have the patience to extract the tiny kernels, is responsible for its name. The pinyon jay is a social bird, even during the nesting season, and several nests may be found within a small area. When not breeding, these jays are great rovers, appearing suddenly where least expected and even wandering out over the sage-covered foothills. At such times their clear, ringing flock call is audible for long distances. The pinyon jay is a powerful flier and not averse to crossing wide expanses of open country. In this respect it is more like a crow than a true jay.

The scrub jays, including the varieties known as the Florida and the California jay, are, as the name suggests, partial to areas of scrubby or chaparral vegetation. They are found from the western United States south into Mexico, and also, as an isolated colony, in the palmetto and oak scrub of Florida.

Closely allied to the blue jay and Steller's jay, the scrub jay (Plates 87, 88) differs from these others chiefly in that it is more slender and lacks a crest. The Florida scrub

(Continued on page 145)

110

*California Thrasher. It lives on the ground beneath
dense brush or chaparral and runs
rapidly about in search of food.*

*Brown Thrasher. A well-known summer bird in the East, it lives in undergrowth but sings
from loftier perches. Sometimes confused with the plumper, shorter-tailed wood thrush.*

111

112

*Bendire's Thrasher. Perhaps the most obscurely
colored thrasher of our southwestern deserts.
It is quite common in Arizona.*

*Curved-billed Thrasher. A good-sized bird generally seen perched on an organ-
pipe cactus or similar vantage point in the deserts of the Southwest.*

113

114

Long-billed Thrasher. Found in south Texas and northeast Mexico, Sennett's thrasher, as it used to be called, is closely related to the brown thrasher.

Mockingbird. Famous songster and mimic found all across the southern United States.

115

116

Catbird. It often places its nest four to eight feet above the ground in shrubbery near a home. When its nest is approached, it protests vociferously.

117

Golden-crowned Kinglet. It builds a snug, feather-lined nest to protect its tiny eggs.

118

Ruby-crowned Kinglet. A very small songster usually identified by the twitching of its wings as it hops about searching for tiny insects.

119

Wood Thrush. In constructing its nest this thrush uses mud almost as freely as its cousin, the robin; it may also include pieces of paper, cellophane, and cloth.

120

Olive-backed Thrush. In the East this thrush is found only near the Canadian border; in the West it nests southward to California.

121
*Veery or Wilson's Thrush.
Loves moist woodlands and
nests on the ground.*

*Hermit Thrush. Frequently described as the most gifted songster in North America,
it has often inspired poets. It usually sings only in its northern nesting grounds.*

122

123

Mountain Bluebird. The eggs, blue like the bird itself, range from four to seven in number. The nest, made of grass and weed stems, is placed in a cavity.

124

Common Bluebird. Its lovely colors and soft, warbling call make this species a universal favorite.

Western Bluebird. Also known as the chestnut-backed bluebird, this species is common in many areas on the West Coast. The absence, so far, of starlings in this region leaves the western bluebird in undisputed possession of birdhouses.

126

*Cedar Waxwing. The one shortcoming of this demure-looking,
attractive bird is that it has no true song.*

127
*American Robin.
The camera catches
it in mid-flight.*

128
*American Robin. This
abundant species is now
expanding its range in the
South and the West.*

129

Starling. An introduced bird that has become a pest but has cheerful whistles and can even learn to talk.

130

Loggerhead Shrike. Although similar to many songbirds in size and appearance, it is fierce, killing birds and snakes.

Phainopepla. In contrast to this modestly colored female, the male is a flashing black and white. It is related to the waxwings.

131

132

Red-eyed Vireo. A very common summer bird in the broad-leaved woods of the Northeast.

133
*Yellow-throated Vireo.
Prefers roadside shade
trees and open woodlands
for a summer home.*

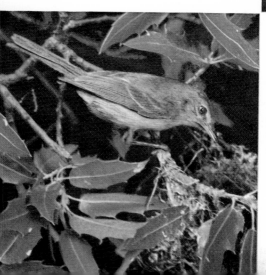

134
*Bell's Vireo. Named by Audubon
after John G. Bell, a taxidermist
who accompanied him to the
Upper Missouri.*

135

Warbling Vireo. It would rarely be noticed as it hops about in the upper limbs of tall shade trees were it not for a warbling song uttered incessantly throughout the summer.

Solitary Vireo. One of the most handsome of the species. A rich, alto quality makes its song seem more melodious than that of most other vireos.

136

137

Yellow Warbler. Its nest is often lined with downy material from ferns.

138

Myrtle Warbler. A common warbler that sometimes winters in the North.

139

Kentucky Warbler. More of a ground-dweller than most warblers.

140

Prairie Warbler. Actually doesn't inhabit grassy prairies but pine barrens or other dry, brushy vegetation.

141

Mourning Warbler. So called because of black hood across chest of male.

142

Kirtland's Warbler. Although it nests only in Michigan and winters only in the Bahamas, it is seldom seen while migrating.

143

*Cape May Warbler.
Watchers prize a
glimpse of it.*

144

*Blackburnian Warbler. Easily
spotted while it is migrating,
it becomes difficult to
see at its nest high
among evergreens.*

145

*Hooded Warbler. Lives in the
undergrowth of well-watered
woodlands.*

146

*Lucy's Warbler. A rather
timid bird of thickets
and low trees, it is
easily overlooked.*

jay (Plate 91) is amazingly bold and impudent, but at the same time thoroughly ingratiating. It hops about with little regard for man, its sharp inquisitive eyes taking in everything. With very little coaxing it will perch on one's head or shoulders. At its nest, it seems to be quite without fear; in fact one can stroke the back of the mother as she broods her eggs or young. At such times she may seize a finger of an intruding hand in her bill—but without pinching hard. Yet, if trapped or handled away from the nest, the same bird will bite and peck viciously.

Observers have noticed that more than two seemingly grown birds sometimes help feed a brood of young jays. Possibly the strangers at the nest are immature or nonbreeding birds which, like little girls with dolls, play at raising a family.

The Canada jay of the great evergreen forests of Canada and the northernmost parts of the United States is a brownish, white-fronted bird which boldly enters the camp of the woodsman and pilfers whatever it can find. In the depth of the northern winter, the presence of any lively feathered visitor is welcome. Lumberjacks have bestowed upon it the rowdy name whisky jack, alleged to be a corruption of an Indian name—*wiskijon*.

Magpies and Nutcrackers

Magpies are, in a sense, glorified jays with long tail feathers. The blue magpie, so commonly depicted in Chinese art, is but one of many colorful tropical species. In northern areas the only species is the black-billed magpie, which ranges from England to Siberia and into western North America. Over this great area it varies little in appearance or habits. The yellow-billed magpie (Plate 93) is found in the interior valleys of California. Its smaller size and yellow bill distinguish this California species from the common American magpie. The yellow-bill nests in colonies in tall trees, while the black-billed magpie nests in solitary pairs, placing its bulky, domed dwelling at an elevation of five or ten feet in a bush or a thick low tree.

In feeding habits, as in size, magpies are somewhat intermediate between jays and ravens. Like the latter, they visit slaughter-houses to devour carrion. Dr. Elliott Coues, pioneer American ornithologist, author of the famous *Key to North American Birds*, wrote of finding six or eight dead magpies at the carcass of a horse he had poisoned to kill wolves. When pressed for food, magpies sometimes alight on horses to peck at saddle sores or other cuts. Because of this habit and because of their occasional pilfering of eggs, young chickens, and quail, this bird is often disliked by farmers. But although a nuisance around isolated western ranches, the colorful and conspicuous magpies enliven the bleak regions in which they dwell.

Clark's nutcracker (Plate 94), a bird of the Rocky Mountains, derives its name from the adeptness with which it cracks open nuts with its powerful bill. This bird is another of the discoveries of the Lewis and Clark Expedition. Its harsh, penetrating cry reverberates across the snow fields and boulder-covered slopes. Early in the spring, when the snow still lies deep in the mountain passes, the nutcracker builds a sturdy

145

nest in a pine or spruce and lines it thickly with bark and feathers so that the cold cannot penetrate it and freeze the eggs.

Crows and Ravens

The crow (Plate 95) is found throughout much of North America, but is absent from wilderness areas. It is one of the sliest of birds; although shot and destroyed at every opportunity, it manages to survive in vast numbers. The unpopularity of the crow is a result of its taste for corn and for the eggs and young of game birds and songbirds. Yet

Brown Creeper

it accomplishes much for man by destroying cutworms and other grubs.

Like its relative the blue jay, the crow is mischievous and is fond of persecuting owls, if it can find them during the daytime. At night the roles are reversed and the great horned owl sometimes catches crows as they sleep. In winter, crows gather each night at immense roosts, comprising thousands of birds. With the advent of spring they break up into pairs, each couple building a large nest in a tree. Often taken as pets when young, crows sometimes learn to speak a few words. The widespread belief that a crow's tongue must be split before it can talk is nonsense, perhaps derived from the fact that normally the tongue is slightly split at the tip. Although amusing, pet crows have an annoying habit of hiding any small bright object they may chance upon.

The fish crow of the Atlantic Coast is recognized by its quavering, high-pitched call. It is somewhat smaller than the American crow and is even fonder of the eggs of other birds.

The common raven, a larger cousin of the crow, is found over much of North America southward to the plateau of Mexico, as well as in Asia and Europe. Its doleful croaking and sable plumes have made it a symbol of disaster. It is primarily a bird of the wilderness; when cultivation comes, the raven disappears and the crow moves in. The raven usually places its nest on the ledge of a cliff and lays three to five mottled greenish-gray eggs.

The only other North American raven is the so-called white-necked raven found in the arid plains of the southwestern United States and northern Mexico. It is a sociable bird. Like the common raven, it often soars about high in the sky, either for pleasure or in order to watch for food. The epithet "white-necked" is misleading, for only the bases of the neck feathers are white, and these are normally not visible; the scientific name *cryptoleucus*, which suggests cryptic or hidden white, is more accurate.

Titmice 16

The titmice are a family of Old World birds which presumably entered North America by the Bering Sea route. There have been times when the lowering of sea level, owing to the retention of vast quantities of water in continental ice caps, has exposed a broad connection between Siberia and Alaska. Land bridges as an explanation of the distribution of animals and plants are no longer popular as hypotheses, but the Bering Sea bridge is one about which geologists, zoologists, and botanists are generally in agreement. By that avenue many groups of trees, mammals, and countless other organisms, probably including man himself, originally entered the New World from the Old. A less conspicuous exchange in the opposite direction also took place.

The titmice have not reached South America, nor have nearly as many types developed in North America as are present in their Eurasian homeland. The verdin of our Southwest represents a distinctly American evolutionary product, but some of our other titmice, such as the familiar black-capped chickadee, are almost exact counterparts of forms still existing across the whole Old World land mass from China to the British Isles.

Titmice are attractive birds from man's point of view, and many kinds, such as the little tomtit of Gilbert and Sullivan's *Mikado*, have entered richly into folklore. Some of them nest freely as man's "tenants"; there is a record of an earthen bottle strapped to the branches of a tree at Oxbridge, England, that was occupied by families of blue titmice for 110 years. On the other hand, fruit growers are prejudiced against certain titmice because of the contention that they are bud eaters. Investigation has shown, however, that the buds attacked almost invariably harbored grubs!

The chickadees, named from their call by the eastern woodland Indians, are the most widely known of American titmice. The black-capped chickadee (Plate 96) breeds from coast to coast across the northern two-thirds of the United States and northward into Canada and Alaska. It is the tamest American bird. Like many other titmice, it forms wandering bands, except during the nesting season. Such groups are more than ordinarily sociable. Not only do the members keep in constant touch with one another, but they also seem to serve as a focus or magnet for many other kinds of small birds. At the time of spring or autumn migration, there is no better way to observe a variety of wood warblers than to sit near a troupe of chickadees and retain their interest by "squeaking" or by whistling their high, double-noted "phoebe" call.

Black-capped Chickadee — PARUS ATRICAPILLUS

I T IS in the winter that we know the chickadee best. It appears to be the most fearless of our birds. Rare is the suet that does not attract a party of these hardy mites; with a little patience one can even encourage them to come to hand. There are few bird journals or family magazines which have not at one time or another shown photographs of children more or less festooned with these "cheerful" little birds . . .

The fiercest weather does not seem to bother them. This is a matter of physiology. Compared to a man, a bird is internally a raging inferno. The chickadee's heart, for example, beats five-hundred times a minute when the bird is *asleep* and about twice that when it is exercising. This, compared to our sluggardly, near-reptilian seventy to eighty beats a minute is a good indication why a small bird must eat almost constantly just to stay alive. Cold does not bother a winter bird; lack of food does. If the fires are kept supplied with fuel, the bird's high-power metabolism — plus layers of loose, fluffy, insulating feathers — keep it going . . .

The black-capped chickadee is thought to be the same species as the European willow tit; the phrase *tit-willow* is not included in the repertoire of either. The common call from which this bird gets its name is known to everyone. The so-called "spring" song, *phoebe*, can be heard at any season, and it is reported that "sixteen different vocalizations" have been listed.

— *John A. Livingston in*
BIRDS OF THE EASTERN FOREST, VOL. II

This card is sold for the benefit of the conservation program of
THE CANADIAN AUDUBON SOCIETY, 46 ST. CLAIR AVENUE EAST,
TORONTO 7, CANADA

Christmas Greetings

and all good wishes for a

Happy New Year

Black-capped chickadees are hardy creatures, able to endure the most severe winter weather as long as they can find fuel enough during each short day to keep their "high-speed engines" running. The northerly members of the species are somewhat migratory, and in middle latitudes a larger population of them is more likely to be found in winter than during the breeding season. The birds clamber and hang, either side up, in their search for the eggs of plant lice, tree crickets, moths, and spiders, or they turn to such vegetable products as seeds and berries. Plant food may comprise half their fare in winter, but with the advent of spring they resume the battle against caterpillars, moths, plant lice, beetles, and other insects, upon which the young are almost exclusively fed. To see a diminutive chickadee put the quietus on a huge caterpillar by swinging and banging it repeatedly against a bough is to realize that, despite its fluffy charm, it is a quite ferocious "bird of prey."

Chickadees nest in holes. Dead gray birches, in which the half-rotten wood is held intact by sound and leathery bark, suit them to perfection. They dig a cavity and line it with grass and plant down, lay any number of eggs up to nine or ten, and rear a family which expands as it grows until one wonders how so many nestlings can live or breathe in so tight a space. Not content with one brood in a season, a pair

Cactus Wren

of chickadees usually rears a second and sometimes a third.

The Carolina chickadee of the Southeast and central South is a distinct species from the black-cap, although the differences in appearance and behavior are slight. The ear is worth more than the eye in telling the two apart, for the tone of voice is not the same in the two species. The geographical dividing line between the species is, however, remarkably sharp. On the Atlantic Coast it is marked by the Raritan River, New Jersey.

In the West another species, the mountain chickadee, is found, where it ranges from Lower California to British Columbia and as far eastward as western Texas. This bird is in all respects "chickadeean," differing in appearance from the foregoing kinds chiefly in possessing a white eyebrow stripe that cuts into the black crown.

Brown-capped chickadees (Plate 97) differ from the black-cap by their coloring, as indicated by the name, and also by their hoarse, whispering utterance of *chickadee*. They inhabit the great northern forests to the borders of the tundra. Farther south we see them only as casual winter visitors, when they mingle, chickadeelike, with nuthatches, woodpeckers, and other hardy birds. Conifer seeds supply part of their winter food but, like other titmice, they are mainly insect eaters.

The tufted titmouse (Plate 102), a gray, crested bird with a white under surface and reddish-brown flanks, has the contour of a tiny blue jay. The sexes are alike in appearance, as in the chickadees. This bird occurs on the Atlantic Coast from New Jersey southward to Florida and westward a little

Bewick's Wren

beyond the Mississippi. One of the so-called Carolinian species, its range on the coast stops with extraordinary abruptness. It is common, for example, on Staten Island, which is one of the boroughs of New York City, but is virtually unknown on Long Island, only a mile or so away across the Narrows. The tufted titmouse never seems to tire of whistling *peter* and *deedle,* winter and summer. Like the cardinal, it is non-migratory and therefore an all-year neighbor. Its apparent cheerfulness, smart garb, and fondness for, or tolerance of, man's settlements, make it a universal favorite. Its life history is in general like that of the chickadees, although it is big enough to handle beech mast and acorns as part of its winter food.

West of the range of the tufted titmouse, in eastern and central Texas and southward into Mexico, the black-crested titmouse lives wherever there are plenty of trees. The two species are close relatives and interbreed to some extent. Still farther west, between the Rocky Mountains and the Pacific, the plain titmouse (Plate 101), well named *inornatus,* differs from its relatives in the unmarked brownish gray of the upper part of its body.

The verdin (Plate 99) is a small bird

quite different from any titmouse thus far listed. The adult male has a yellow head, greenish back, white belly, and a reddish epaulet, duller than that of the red-winged blackbird. The female is paler in color and the young are very plain and mousy. The verdin's call notes are, however, quite chickadeelike, and its energetic actions and feeding habits are altogether "titmousy." Here the resemblance ends, for the verdin likes semidesert country, such as is found between southern Texas and southern California, and it inhabits thickets of cactus and mesquite, often far from water. Its nest, twice the diameter of the bird's total length, is a well-lined ball of twigs built around the terminal fork of a branch. The entrance is on the side. The verdin does not migrate but sleeps through the winter nights in an old or supplementary nest, where it is protected from the chill that descends over the desert at nightfall.

Finally, the bush-tit, of which numerous races have been described, is a gray and "Quakerish" little titmouse of the Pacific Coast and the Rocky Mountains, from Oregon to Mexico and eastward as far as western Texas. It is perhaps the smallest American bird, with the exception of the hummingbirds. The most notable attribute of the bush-tit is its nest, which almost outdoes that of the Baltimore oriole. It is a long bag of mosses, fibers, lichens, tree blossoms, and feathers, with the entrance near the top. The hang birds, as bush-tits are called in California, suspend these conspicuous gray purses from thicketed oaks, ashes, willows, and other trees, and deposit in them up to nine white eggs. Their food habits are like those of chickadees, and the proportion of

scale insects eaten makes the bush-tit economically important throughout much of its range.

Nuthatches and Creepers 17

Four nuthatches are found in North America: the red-breasted, the white-breasted, the brown-headed, and the pygmy. The red-breast is also present in Asia and a species very closely allied to the white-breast is likewise found there. More exclusively American are the sociable little brown-headed nuthatches of the pine forests of southeastern United States and the pygmy nuthatch of the West. The latter travels far into the South, and has been seen near timberline at the Pass of Cortez above Mexico City.

Nuthatches are hardy birds and stay in the North throughout the coldest months of the winter. This is especially true of the white-breasted nuthatch (Plate 98); the red-breast is partly migratory. Nuthatches are not noted as songsters, although the white-breast has a mellow trill. They have characteristic nasal call notes which they utter as they climb around on the trunks and limbs of trees in search of insects. They are more agile and acrobatic at such activities than any other birds and can hop down a trunk head first with perfect ease. Unlike woodpeckers and brown creepers, the tail

151

of the nuthatch is short and is not used as a prop in climbing. In addition to insects and their eggs and larvae, nuthatches feed on various seeds. The name nuthatch is derived from their habit of wedging nuts in crannies where they can use the bill like a hatchet to "hatch" open the shells. Nuthatches are regular visitors at winter feeding stations, where they are rather aggressive towards other birds. They eat suet and are very fond of doughnuts.

Nuthatches lay a clutch of six to eight spotted eggs in a cranny in a tree. The European nuthatch plasters mud around the entrance to its nest hole until a slit remains that is barely adequate to admit the bird to its nest. This practice probably excludes some enemies from the nest. The late Joseph Grinnell, the well-known California ornithologist, made the interesting suggestion that the white breast of the nuthatch serves as a reflector to throw a little additional light into the dark nooks in which it may be nesting or searching for food.

The creepers are a small family of birds of which only one species, the brown creeper, is found in North America. It is a slender, streaked bird about seven inches long, usually seen as it creeps up the trunks of trees in search of minute insects and their eggs. Arriving near the top, it flutters like a falling brown leaf to the base of another tree and repeats the process. The tail feathers, pointed and stiffened in woodpecker fashion, serve as a prop as it hitches its way along. Brown creepers are typical members of the small parties of woodland birds of late autumn and winter, flocks that also include chickadees, nuthatches, woodpeckers, and kinglets. The nest of the brown creeper is built of twigs and is placed beneath a large, loose slab of bark.

Kinglets and Gnatcatchers 18

Kinglets are tiny woodland birds. In one of the two species illustrated here, the ruby-crowned kinglet (Plate 118), the crown patch is concealed except when the bird is displaying. On the other hand, the golden-crowned kinglet (Plate 117) has a broad, conspicuous orange crown stripe, flanked by black lines. The two kinglets are quite different in their vocal powers. The golden-crown's best efforts are limited to weak lisping notes, but the ruby-crown has a rich, full-bodied warbling song that is the more surprising when one considers the tiny size of its source. Kinglets are hardy little birds; the golden-crown sometimes stays in the North throughout the winter, associating with chickadees, nuthatches, and other insectivorous winter birds.

The blue-gray gnatcatcher (Plates 103, 104) is a tiny, restless bird with a long tail which, like the wren, it often holds vertically above its back. It lives in the South and builds a beautiful, lichen-covered nest resembling an old knot or protuberance on a branch. In the Southwest and in Mexico, gnatcatchers are common birds in the thorny chaparral. They utter whining or grating notes as they move through the brush in small parties, often in the company of titmice and migrant warblers.

Both the kinglets and gnatcatchers belong to the true warblers, or Sylviidae, a family that is much more numerous in the Old World than in the New.

Wrens   19

The house wren (Plate 109) is one of the few birds known, at least by name, to many who have no particular interest in wildlife. Wren houses, the little "bungalows" with the tiny entrances and peaked roofs, are almost a standard item of outdoor furniture in many suburban communities. Jenny wren, as she is popularly called, is the only cavity dweller small enough to enter these little houses. She crams into the box a bulky nest of twigs. Wrens are pugnacious and do not like close neighbors, even when these be other wrens, and they sometimes visit the nests of such neighbors and puncture the eggs. They thus exemplify the theory of a pioneer British student of birds, Eliot Howard, that each pair of birds stakes out a domain from which it ejects all competing visitors, particularly others of the same species. Usually it is the male who selects a territory, which he announces by driving away interlopers and by singing. The female takes a more passive attitude. Probably it is the same with wrens, although the bestowal of the name Jenny wren upon the species might suggest that wren society is matriarchal. The male wren utters his bubbling song incessantly, while "Jenny" chatters and scolds all and sundry.

The late Dr. S. Prentice Baldwin, a pioneer of bird-banding research, made a special study of the "marriage" relations of the house wren. He put up numerous bird houses and banded all the wrens using them. He found that the wrens, which raise two or three broods a year, often change mates between each brood. It is probably erroneous to interpret this frequent change of mates—which is, by the way, characteristic of many small birds—as meaning that the members of a pair quickly tire of each other, or that they share the human delusion that "the far hills are greener." It indicates merely that no permanent bonds develop between the pair: they perform instinctively the sequence of cooperative acts involved in selecting a home, building a nest, hatching a clutch of eggs, and rearing a brood of young—but that is all. Between broods there is a brief period of reduced interest in nesting, and at this time the two members of a pair often drift apart. When they are again in the mood for nesting, the first potential mate that comes along is acceptable.

Several other species of wrens are found within the confines of the United States. The winter wren is the hardiest of the lot and sometimes lingers through the winter, even in the North. It is the epitome of wren characteristics: chunky, with a conspicuous tail which it holds pertly erect above its back. Its song is very melodious. This is the only member of the wren family that has reached the Old World. The Carolina wren

(Plate 107) is a larger species, common in the South, where its loud song is one of the prominent bird voices. The rock wren and the canyon wren (Plate 108) are western species. To hear the sweet and haunting song of the canyon wren in America, one must visit ravines or gullies, but in Mexico City the adobe buildings provide a good substitute for canyons, and the song of this bird is heard in the city streets. The long-billed marsh wren (Plate 105) is found not in deserts or canyons but in large swamps.

The largest of the American wrens and one of the least typical is the speckled cactus wren (Plate 106) of the Southwest. Its loud rasping calls are ever-present among the cholla and other large desert cacti, but unlike most wrens it is a poor songster.

The dipper or water ouzel (Plate 100) is, in many ways, wrenlike, although some think it closer to the thrushes. This remarkable bird inhabits rushing streams in the Rocky Mountains, plunging fearlessly into the water in search of caddis-fly larvae and other aquatic insects. It builds a moss nest on a rock or under a bridge. A hardy bird, it stays as far north as it can find open, running water. The dipper is a fine singer.

Mockingbirds and   20
Thrashers

A southern plantation, magnolias, a mockingbird (Plate 115) singing in the moonlight from the ridgepole of a log cabin —this is an authentic vignette of American life. The mocker abounds from Florida to California, but northern winters are too cold for its liking. Its song contains snatches of the melodies of many other species, all blended into a harmonious and prolonged composition.

For those who live north of the range of the mockingbird, its cousins, the thrashers and the catbird, must serve as substitutes. The brown thrasher (Plate 111) has the habit of repeating each phrase of its song before going on to the next one. Thrashers only occasionaly mimic other birds. The brown thrasher is one of the first birds to cease singing in the summer. As soon as its nesting is well under way it falls silent, except for the heavy *tschunk* of alarm, uttered when someone ventures near its concealed nest. In late summer the brown thrasher sometimes gives forth a soft warbling song hardly recognizable as coming from this species, while the crissal thrasher, a related western species, sings rather freely in late October. The long-billed thrasher (Plate 114) of Texas is a very close relative of the brown thrasher.

Thrashers, mockingbirds, and catbirds are all slender, long-tailed, brush-dwelling birds. They build a cup-shaped nest and lay three or four eggs, which may be plain blue, as in the catbird and crissal thrasher, or speckled with brown as in the mockingbird and in most of the other thrashers.

The thrashers of the southwestern deserts—the crissal, the curve-billed (Plate 113), the Bendire's (Plate 112), the California (Plate 110), and the Leconte's—are more terrestrial than other members of the family. With a side sweep of the head, they send the sand flying with their long bills and in this way uncover insects. These thrashers, like most desert birds, are pale. grayish brown, matching the arid landscape. They thread through the thorny vegetation at a great speed; the crissal thrasher is especially rapid, proceeding over the ground by long hops, aided now and then by a quick flip of its wings.

The catbird (Plate 116) is slaty gray with a blackish cap. It is one of the best known dooryard birds of the East, where it nests in shrubbery and hedges. Although it keeps out of sight much of the time, its complaining call, which sounds like the meow of a cat, reveals its presence. The catbird is a persistent singer. Its vocal efforts have a certain similarity to those of its talented cousins, the mockingbirds and thrash-ers, but it often utters squeaky or false notes that rob its song of much of its potential beauty.

Thrushes 21

Thrushes are among the most widely distributed of all small birds. They are found on every continent; they cross the Arctic Circle in both Eurasia and North America, and extend southward over the tropics virtually to Cape Horn. They are found on most islands, frequently as endemic species, even as far from the great land masses as

Bohemian Waxwings

mid-ocean. The family is not easily defin-able because it intergrades with other groups of songbirds, particularly with Old World warblers and flycatchers. This is a familiar characteristic throughout the great order of perching birds because they prob-ably went through most of their evolution during the geologically recent period called the Age of Mammals. In any event, the diffi-culties in classifying thrushes and thrushlike birds in America are not as great as in other parts of the earth. Nearly all American thrushes, however, are typical members of the group, even though some of them are close kin to European and Asiatic species; others, such as the bluebirds, belong to sub-divisions of the family that originated in America.

The thrushes are soft-billed in compari-son with the finches; their diet is therefore made up mostly of insects and other small invertebrates and a wide variety of soft or pulpy fruits that the birds can swallow whole. The thrush family includes some of the finest songsters.

The American robin (Plates 127, 128) is a typical thrush. It is, in fact, the closest relative of the European blackbird, *Turdus merula merula,* from which Turdidae, the scientific name of the thrush family, is de-rived. One might say that the famous black-bird of Britain (no relation to the American blackbirds) is merely a robin that has been dipped in India ink! The way in which the American bird acquired the name of the smaller European thrush or chat known as "robin redbreast" has been described in the Introduction.

Robins breed over most of North Amer-ica, from coast to coast and from Mexico to Alaska. They are migratory—yet the bulk of them winter to the north of the southern boundary of the United States. No birds have profited more by the opening up of the primitive country, for the robin was never a denizen of dense forest. It rapidly became a farm and orchard bird, and it is now par excellence the most familiar native bird of suburban surroundings and city parks.

The robin's taste for earthworms lures it to lawns as soon as spring thaws have melted the frozen ground. Whether sight or sound or touch enables the bird to find its subter-ranean victims is a much-argued question— and one that has not yet been fully settled. The manner in which a worm-hunting robin cocks its head is sufficient to convince at least the uncritical that it is listening to what is going on beneath the sod. A remarkably handsome bird, as might be more generally recognized if it were less common, the robin arrives early in spring and stays late in the fall — if it leaves at all. Living intimately with friendly human beings, the bird carols merrily from dawn until nightfall. It scolds cats, shares with man his cherries—when it can't eat all of them — lays four eggs of a lovely color that everybody recognizes, rears in its reinforced mud nest two broods of speckle-breasted young (which thus be-tray their conventional thrush ancestry), and quite generally suggests that life is both pleasant and successful.

On the Pacific seaboard of North Amer-ica, between northern California and Alaska, the varied thrush inhabits ever-green forests up to high altitudes. One of its common names is "banded robin" which points to its appearance and relationship, although its breast is bright rusty brown,

Starling

almost orange. It is a serene and thrilling vocalist, and Louis Agassiz Fuertes wrote of its wonderfully penetrating song: "It is a single long-drawn note, uttered in several different keys, some of the high-pitched ones with a strong vibrant trill. Each note grows out of nothing, swells to a full tone, and then fades away to nothing until one is carried away with the mysterious song."

Inhabiting large parts of this continent is the group of peculiarly American spotted-breasted thrushes of the genus *Hylocichla*, of which there are five species and more than twice that many geographic races. Some of these birds, which are among the most magnificent of all singers, bear a superficial resemblance to the European song thrush. Four or five hylocichlas, several of

which may look extraordinarily alike, sometimes inhabit a single limited area. Every field ornithologist knows that sharp observation is needed to distinguish the olive-backed from the gray-cheeked thrush; and the hermit thrush, the wood thrush, and the veery are also similar.

The hermit thrush has no fewer than seven subspecies, and three of the other five species have two or more. Considering each type only under its specific heading, however, the thrushes of this group are the following:

The wood thrush (Plate 119) is the biggest and reddest, with large spots on its breast. It is a tree-nesting bird of eastern North America, and it now seems to be following the robin in spreading from wilder-

157

ness to suburbs in which woodland has been preserved. Its range does not extend as far north as that of the next three species.

The hermit thrush (Plate 122) is a smaller bird with more diffuse spotting and a rufous tail. It nests on the ground, mostly in mountain forest, from the southern Appalachians to Alaska. The eastern race also has a somewhat unusual nesting area in the flat pitch-pine country of Long Island and Cape Cod. Nobody has yet been able to explain this curious departure from the general pattern of its life history. It is a hardy bird and the only one of the thrushes in its group that commonly winters within the United States.

The olive-backed (Plate 120) and gray-cheeked thrushes are brown, rather than foxy, with spotting similar to that of the hermit thrush. The olive-back has a ring of light feathers around the eye, which is its best identification mark. The distribution of each is rather similar to that of the hermit thrush, although the gray-cheek is even more northerly, attaining the edge of stunted spruce-fir forest in Alaska and across Bering Strait in Siberia. Both thrushes usually nest in evergreen trees, although the nest of the gray-cheek is sometimes built in low ground cover.

The veery (Plate 121) is the palest member of the group, with only faint breast spots. The northward extension of its range stops short of that of the three preceding thrushes. It exhibits a liking for watery places, commonly nesting on the ground near a stream.

The wood thrush and the veery are the only members of this group likely to be seen or heard in thickly settled country; the others are typically birds of the forest. One could readily fill a volume with what has been written about their songs, but reading such descriptions is a poor substitute for hearing them. All have a quality justly described as ethereal. The hermit thrush doubtless takes the palm, but the wood thrush and even the veery have their partisans. In each of these three, every species contributes something that the others lack. The song of the wood thrush is in some respects the richest, mellowest, and roundest; the whirling bell-like tones of the veery are perhaps the most elfin; the song of the hermit thrush has been very simply described by Richard H. Pough, of the American Museum of Natural History, in these words: "The long, low, flutelike opening note is followed by up to a dozen shorter, thinner notes varying slightly in pitch, and run together in groups to give a tremolo effect. As the cadences continue, the openings tend to go so high as to approach the limit of audibility." Some of the notes may, it should be pointed out, transcend audibility to human ears, but perhaps not to the singer's hidden mate and to rival males, of which four or five can occasionally be heard from other treetops roundabout.

The bluebirds are another fundamentally American group. They are universal favorites. John Burroughs's reference to the sky on the back and the rich earth on the breast of the common bluebird (Plate 124) may have become hackneyed with repetition, but it is still a meaningful metaphor.

Bluebirds, like robins, flock in winter to the Southern states and comb the woods in search of insects and small clinging fruits. By April they come north, even as far as

New England, and pair and nest early, seeking such cavities as old woodpecker burrows, knot holes in the siding of farmhouses, or man-proffered boxes. The introduced starling, unfortunately, now offers all too effective competition. The breeding range of the bluebird stretches from Florida and the Gulf Coast to Newfoundland, westward to the eastern base of the Rocky Mountains, and south into the mountains of Mexico.

The western or chestnut-backed bluebird (Plate 125) of the Rocky Mountains and the Pacific seaboard is a distinct species. It is purplish blue and chestnut on the back, purplish blue on the throat, and darker on the breast than its eastern cousin. Its habits are similar except that it ranges to altitudes far higher than any in the mountains of the East.

Most striking of all is the mountain bluebird (Plate 123), which breeds from the high mountains of California northward to southern Yukon. The male is pale purplish blue above and pale greenish blue below. The female is much duller, as among all the bluebirds. This species has been reported beyond timberline in country more than thirteen thousand feet above sea level.

Barely getting into the North American fauna is the wheatear, an Old World thrush of plumage that is brownish and inconspicuous except for the white rump and tail, the

White-Eyed Vireo at Nest

latter ending in a black inverted T. Races of this species breed in Alaska, other parts of Arctic America, and Greenland. Living north of tree line, like pipits, they are, of course, ground birds. Wheatears usually migrate back to the Old World, but occasional stragglers are seen on the Atlantic Coast as far south as Long Island.

The Townsend's solitaire of the Rockies is the only North American member of another group of thrushes celebrated for melodious songs. It is a plain-colored bird with two light wing bars and conspicuous white outer webs on the tail quills. The bill is rather wide and flat for a thrush, and its behavior in the air is quite reminiscent of a flycatcher. On the ground its gait resembles a robin's, especially when it runs.

This bird has close relatives inhabiting the peaks of Central America and some of the mountainous islands of the West Indies. It has long been in demand as a songbird in European aviaries. To hear the native solitaire perform, one needs to be equipped for rigorous hikes to lofty mountain gardens. Amid such surroundings the beauty of its song is enhanced and seems superior to that of its caged relatives in Mexico and Cuba.

very much like larks, they were formerly called titlarks. One of the two American species, Sprague's pipit, was named the Missouri skylark by its discoverer, John James Audubon, who encountered it on his expedition to the Missouri River. The other species is the so-called American pipit. Since it is also found in Eurasia, this is a misleading name; perhaps the name used in Europe, rock pipit, should be adopted.

The rock pipit nests in the North and at high elevations in the South, from Maine to the mountains of New Mexico and Arizona. On migration it is distributed throughout the United States, frequenting sand bars and open flats often near rivers and lakes.

The wagtails are related to the pipits, although they are somewhat larger and have longer tails. One species, the yellow wagtail, reaches western Alaska, but it is more widely distributed in the Old World, the true home of this group of birds. In the winter the Alaska yellow wagtail migrates back to Asia, whence it reached the New World, rather than south into Canada and the Western states. Such retracing of an ancestral route of dispersal by later generations of migrant birds is a common phenomenon.

Pipits and Wagtails 22

Pipits are ground-living birds that dwell on grassy plains. In appearance and habits

Shrikes 23

Shrikes are the only American songbirds that have adopted the predatory way of life

(Continued on page 177)

147

*Golden-winged Warbler.
Lays five or six spotted
eggs in a bulky nest
built on the ground.*

148

Chestnut-sided Warbler. It nests in briars.

149

*Nashville Warbler. Quick,
nervous movements characterize
this warbler. Old upland fields
grown up to gray birches are its
favorite nesting place.*

150

*Black and White Warbler.
It has the climbing ability
of a nuthatch.*

151

*Black-throated Gray Warbler. A quiet,
unobtrusive species, it is one of the
relatively few western warblers.*

152

*Black-throated Green Warbler.
Restless, and sings incessantly.*

Black-throated Blue Warbler. Told by white wing mark.

153

154

*Parula Warbler.
F. M. Chapman
has described its
song as a quaint,
attractive little
gurgling sizzle.*

155

Orange-crowned Warbler.
Often only its chirping
in the underbrush reveals it.

156

Canada Warbler. Sprightly and alert,
it catches insects in flight.

Redstart. Called "Little Candle" in Cuba because it gleams in dark, winter woods.

157

158

Wilson's Warbler. This one was found in a swale in Maine. An old name is "Wilson's Green Black-capped Fly-catching Warbler!"

159

Blue-winged Warbler. A rather inconspicuous warbler generally inhabiting brushy clearings and thickets.

160

Prothonotary Warbler. Nests in hollow stubs above slow-flowing water.

161

Magnolia Warbler. The white band across the middle of the tail is a field mark of this warbler. Also distinctive is the gray cap of the male.

162
Louisiana Water-thrush.
Its loud song can be heard even
above rushing water in rocky glens.

163
Northern Water-thrush. Like
several other streamside
birds. it constantly bobs
and bows its head.

164

Common Yellow-throat. A bird of streamside brush, it will venture into the open to feed its hungry brood.

Ovenbird. A "ground warbler," it has neutral-colored legs and walks rather than hops.

165

166

Yellow-breasted Chat. Often only the weird medley of its call reveals this wary bird.

167

Cowbird. The male assumes strained, grotesque poses as he addresses his squeaky song to the female.

168

Boat-tailed Grackle. It lives in colonies in swamps of the Southeast and is polygamous.

169
*Bobolink. Pointed tail feathers
and a metallic call help to
identify the sparrowlike
female bobolink.*

*Meadowlark. The loud cheery whistle of this open-country bird is often represented
by the syllables "spring-of-the-year." It has a long season of song.*

170

171

Yellow-headed Blackbird. Lives in colonies among bullrushes in the West.

172

Common Redwing. Usually found in swamps, but often nests in hayfields.

173

Brewer's Blackbird. In its nesting colonies females outnumber males, and the latter are often polygamous.

174

Orchard Oriole. In New York and New England, watchers are always eager for a glimpse of this rare bird.

175

Bullock's Oriole. Frequents streamside cottonwoods.

Scott's Oriole. Named for Professor W. D. Scott, pioneer student of Arizona birds.

176

177

Hooded Oriole. The most brilliant of our orioles.

Baltimore Oriole. Often nests in the same elm each year, sometimes right over a road.

178

179

Scarlet Tanager. As soon as the nesting season is over and before migration to South America, the brilliant male molts into a green plumage resembling that of his mate.

Western Tanager. While the female incubates, the male wanders casually through western pine woods, singing at intervals from treetops.

180

181 *Scarlet Tanager. Has a flaming color usually found only in tropical birds.*

182

*Summer Tanager. Most melodious
of the tanagers.*

183

Indigo Bunting. The female shows only a trace of the indigo hue.

184

Indigo Bunting. Perched on a hot sunny hillside the male often sings throughout long summer days.

185

Lark Bunting. In summer this male will be a handsome black and white.

186

Lazuli Bunting. A weaker, more rambling song distinguishes this western species from the related indigo bunting.

characteristic of hawks and owls. Because their feet lack the strong, curved claws of a hawk, shrikes impale their prey upon a thorn. After thus anchoring it, they tear it apart with the hooked beak. For this reason they are often called butcher birds.

The American shrikes are modestly colored gray, black, and white birds. The loggerhead shrike (Plate 130) is a little smaller than a robin, the northern shrike slightly larger. In keeping with its smaller size, the loggerhead shrike eats large insects more frequently than it does mice or birds. The northern shrike is an inveterate foe of field mice and of such birds as chickadees. This is particularly true in the winter, when the ground is deeply covered with snow and food is scarce. At such times the northern shrike invades villages in search of English sparrows, and, attracted by the imprisoned birds, it will even enter the traps operated by bird banders.

Although they do not have the rapid dashing flight of a falcon, shrikes relentlessly pursue small birds through brush and cover until the victims become confused. Sometimes they kill more than they can eat and hang the surplus on thorns or on the barbs of a wire fence. A few years ago residents of a community in North Carolina were surprised to find a locust tree in which no fewer than twenty-one small snakes were impaled upon thorns. Local naturalists concluded that this rather grisly display of dangling reptiles was the "food locker" of a loggerhead shrike, but, as far as the authors know, it has never been proved that the shrike later returns to these food caches, like a squirrel to its hoard of nuts.

Shrikes build a substantial nest of twigs, lined with rootlets. The four or five eggs are gray, mottled with olive and brown. As might be expected, shrikes are belligerent in defense of nest and young. The song of the shrike suggests that of the catbird but is a squeakier and less musical performance. It also has disagreeable scolding notes.

Waxwings and Phainopeplas   24

Waxwings take their name from the terminal knobs on the shafts of their inner wing quills, which look like decorations made of hard and shiny red sealing wax. The cedar waxwing (Plate 126) sometimes has these on the tail as well as the wings.

Waxwings are true "artists' birds," their beauty stemming not from gaudiness but from harmony, design, and contour. They have crested heads, subdued but charmingly accented plumage patterns, and a general look of being sleek and well groomed. Their behavior is also likely to be interpreted from a human point of view as gentle and polite. A row of cedar waxwings, for example, sometimes passes a ripe cherry back and forth from bill to bill before some member of the group finally swallows it. They are, however, certainly not "musicians' birds," for they merely chatter, or emit whistles that suggest escaping steam. In fact, the waxwings are about the least songbird-like of any of the true songbirds.

The Bohemian waxwing is a species that dwells in the northern open forests, nesting from western Canada and Alaska to the edge of the treeless tundra as well as in Lapland. Their winter incursions into the United States are often made in large flocks—more birds, indeed, than can be accounted for by the few known breeding stations. The same is true in Europe, where winter invasions as far west as Britain have been observed and recorded for centuries, although the source of the flocks remained unknown until the first nesting place was discovered in Lapland in 1856. On the irregular occasions when the Bohemian waxwings move southward and eastward, they are not infrequently seen in orchards and city parks.

Most of the habits and behavior characteristics of this relatively little-known waxwing seem to be similar to those of the smaller and more widely distributed cedar waxwing. The latter inhabits the greater part of the United States and southern Canada as a breeding bird. Some members of the population winter as far south as Central America, but the cedar waxwing, like its larger relative, is to some extent an erratic wanderer. Its migrations, unlike those of most American summer resident birds, are not regular as to season, course, and goal. Flocks are likely to appear almost anywhere and at any time outside the nesting season—even in midwinter.

In late spring the larger groups break up into pairs, but it may be deep summer before such mated birds build a nest—not infrequently in an apple orchard—lay and incubate their eggs, and rear their young. The fledglings begin to flock soon after they leave the nest, and in October one encounters roving companies made up mostly or exclusively of youthful birds, distinguishable from the adults by their duller plumage and striped flanks. Their intentness upon the serious business of life appears to make them tame, and one may sometimes approach within a few feet while they are stripping a juicy harvest from a pokeberry.

Fleshy fruits of many kinds, ripe or dried out, make up nearly nine-tenths of the cedar waxwing's diet, and in the northeastern United States juniper or red-cedar berries are a leading staple. The birds can, however, turn heartily to insects, and they are even competent "flycatchers." During mass flights of small forest moths in autumn, the writers have watched cedar birds array themselves along the windward edge of a woodland and make short sallies, hour after hour, to snap up moths. The only other species of waxwing is a native of Japan.

The phainopeplas or silky flycatchers are not related to true flycatchers of either the New or Old Worlds, but seem rather to be cousins of the waxwings. The lone species to enter the United States is a bird of the dry, and even of the near-desert, country of the southwestern United States and of Mexico, inhabiting areas that support mesquite, cactus, and creosote bush. The phainopepla wears a tall, thin crest, which is usually held erect. The male is glossy blue-black all over, except for a conspicuous white patch on the wing quills. The female (Plate 131) is plain brownish gray, but with crest and wing patch similar to her mate's.

Their fruity diet, in which juniper, sumac, and mistletoe berries figure, the dexterity with which phainopeplas take moths and other flying insects, and the crested

Pine Warbler with Young

head, all suggest kinship with the waxwings. Its song, however, sets the phainopepla well apart, for the male has a rather rich repertory of lively, vivacious notes and phrases, some of which have been likened to those of red-wings and meadowlarks.

In this species the male is the chief nest builder. Between home and foraging grounds the birds often fly remarkably high for songbirds. Among the authors' recollections of pack trips in Arizona and adjacent Mexico is that of seeing phainopeplas passing far overhead, occasionally pausing to change course abruptly, and finally making a steep dive into a clump of shrubbery.

Starlings 25

Two species of this Old World family have been successfully introduced into North

America. One of them, the common European starling (Plate 129), abounds in the East and has now reached the Pacific Coast. Although not without engaging attributes, it is, by and large, an unwelcome alien that competes with useful native songbirds and has many destructive habits. The first starlings brought to America were released in New York City in 1890 by one Eugene Schieffelin who, incredible as it may appear, was also one of those responsible for introducing another leading bird pest, the house sparrow, some forty years earlier.

The spread of the starling across America took place after bird watchers were numerous, so that the manner in which it extended its range has been very closely observed. Although a newcomer, it is now one of the most carefully studied of birds all the way from New England to California. It has become more abundant in parts of North America than in any single area of its native Old World home, a development that is all too often true of introduced organisms, whether thistles, Japanese beetles, Hessian flies, carp, or birds.

The starling is a hole-nester, which brings it into competition with such favorite native birds as purple martins, bluebirds, and woodpeckers. For the most part its food habits are, from man's point of view, either neutral or beneficial, and its vocal ability is considerable. Its most unfortunate trait is that it is an aggressive and successful competitor against native species whose company man would much prefer.

In winter, when the starling's iridescent plumage is dabbed all over with light spots, the birds form flocks that feed on agricultural land by day and make flights toward vast roosts, often many miles away, in late afternoon. The returning starlings usually move in small, well-organized groups that fly swiftly and purposefully, sometimes executing remarkable aerial maneuvers as they near their goal. One such nightly roost, on the Metropolitan Museum of Art in New York City, was commonly reputed to number "millions" of starlings. A careful census with mechanical counters reduced this guess to about eight thousand birds, the clamor of which, nevertheless, was a trial to persons residing in the neighborhood. A New York hotel was very nearly put out of business when starlings selected its pseudo-Gothic façade as the site of a similar roost. A reconstruction of the front of this building, eliminating the ledges and niches, finally saved the day.

Another member of the starling family, the crested mynah, a species of southeastern Asia, has become established in British Columbia, in and around the city of Vancouver. Thus far it has spread no further, but its future progress will be watched with close interest by naturalists and by the Fish and Wildlife Service of the United States.

Vireos 26

The red-eyed vireo (Plate 132) is one of the common birds of the broad-leaved forests of eastern North America. Like most vireos it is inconspicuous in coloration. It repeats its simple, loud song endlessly throughout the long summer days. Several other vireos, including the solitary (Plate 136) or blue-headed, the yellow-throated (Plate 133), and the Philadelphia, to mention only eastern species, have similar songs. It requires a good ear and considerable training to tell these songs apart, but it is worth the effort, for the birds live principally in the tops of forest trees and are not always easy to see and recognize by sight. Another widespread species, the warbling vireo (Plate 135), has quite a different song, as does the white-eyed vireo. The latter lives in underbrush rather than in forest trees.

Vireos build a cuplike nest suspended between horizontal forking twigs. That of the red-eyed vireo is often no more than six or eight feet above the ground, although the birds themselves usually feed and sing from higher elevations. Vireos lay three or four spotted eggs; cowbirds often impose upon them by laying eggs in their nests. There is a difference of opinion as to whether the male of the red-eyed vireo aids in the duties of incubation. This is but one of many facts still unknown about our most common birds.

Vireos live almost exclusively upon insects. They are fond of the small caterpillars known as measuring worms. A vireo with one of these worms in its bill will continue its song, pausing briefly between syllables to rub the caterpillar against a limb and finally to swallow it. As with many songbirds, vireos have a second period of song in the autumn. A few years ago, while camping in the foothills of the Great Smoky Mountains during some fine weather in late September, the authors found that yellow-throated vireos were singing almost as loudly and continuously as they do in the spring mating season.

The warbling vireo and the solitary vireo range across the entire American continent. Several species are limited to the West, as others are to the East. Among the western species is the gray vireo, an extremely inconspicuous little bird that may be found on the dry, rocky, brush-covered hillsides of southern Arizona. Bell's vireo (Plate 134), another species of the Southwest, but one which extends east to Indiana, is also an obscurely colored bird. Other vireos, such as the yellow-throated and the blue-headed, are somewhat brighter in hue, but in general the various species of this family are not notable for coloring. The vireos, like the following group, the wood warblers, to which they are thought to be related, are found only in the New World.

Wood Warblers 27

The wood warblers belong only to America and are presumably of tropical origin. Their number, variety, and beauty stand high among the factors that make the temperate-zone bird life of this continent so rich. At the height of the spring migration, about mid-May in the northern United States, it is frequently possible to see twenty-five or more species of wood warblers within a single day. Moreover, the feat can be accomplished in a large park of such cities as Boston or Chicago quite as readily as in wild country. Scarcely any other group of land birds can offer so amazing a variety.

Unlike crows, robins, and flickers, the warblers are, nevertheless, not generally familiar birds. As the late Dr. Frank M. Chapman, curator of birds at the American Museum of Natural History, and author (with many collaborators) of an entire book on North American wood warblers, wrote, "To the uninitiated, their existence is unknown, and when search reveals the before unsuspected fact that our woods are thronged with birds as exquisitely colored as the daintiest tropical forms, we feel as though a new world were opened to us."

Wood warblers are all insect eaters, although some of them, particularly those that do not retreat south of the United States in winter, rely more or less on small fruits, such as those of the bayberry and sumac. Several species make tremendously long migrations, with terminal points as far apart as Alaska and the southern portion of South America.

Biologists believe that the North American wood warblers have undergone a relatively recent and rapid evolution that has produced wide variety in plumage pattern, together with diverse feeding and nesting habits, which tend to eliminate competition among closely related kinds. In eastern North America, there are, for example, about fifteen species of a single genus, *Dendroica*. Anatomically, these are all much alike, and many of them nest in the same areas. But in plumage pattern the males are as distinctive as though they were birds of different families. The adaptive habits of the several species keep them at different and mutually exclusive forest levels which range from the ground to the upper branches of the tallest trees.

The wood warblers also have many variations in their style of feeding. A few take insects on the wing; some peer and search carefully through foliage, twigs, and crevices of bark; others are rapid flitters, picking off caterpillars and other insects in stride; still others feed mostly among the dead leaves of the woodland floor or along the mossy banks of brooks.

Despite their name, there are only a few notable songsters in the warbler family, although the simple refrains of some, such as the black-throated green warbler, have a pleasing and remarkably haunting quality.

Some warblers are very widespread, whereas others occupy extremely limited territory. Thus, in the southeastern United States, a number of species nesting in the mountains of Arizona, New Mexico, or southeastern California are barely members of the avifauna of the United States. Few observers may have an opportunity to become acquainted with them unless they journey to Mexico or even Central America, the principal range of these birds.

California, a state wealthy in birds, has few wood warblers compared, for example, with Massachusetts, because they are about twice as numerous in the eastern half of the continent as in the western. The black and white warbler (Plate 150), on the other hand, a bird of extremely dressy even though simple plumage, is distributed nearly everywhere that trees grow, from the Atlantic Coast westward to the fringes of the Rocky Mountains. It is a bark creeper

182

and a gleaner, proclaiming title to its chosen territory by a rudimentary song which sounds like the forward and backward strokes of a small handsaw. The black and white warbler nests on the ground under a lean-to of dead leaves.

The prothonotary warbler (Plate 160), pompously named for a livery resembling churchly vestments, is a lovely little golden or orange-yellow bird with slate-gray wings and tail—in some ways reminiscent of a diminutive oriole. Its colors are hardly protective, for it fairly gleams in the dark shadows of river forests in its South American winter range. In the northern half of the hemisphere, it is also a bird of damp woods near water, and is seen chiefly in the southeastern third of the United States. It builds its nest in a woodpecker or chickadee hole, or sometimes under a slab of bark. The female builds it, the male merely fetching up the "bricks and mortar" in the form of fine grass, shreds of bark, moss, feathers, and hair. Its song is high-pitched and penetrating, but with no great musical virtuosity.

Swainson's warbler, a plainly colored species of a pattern somewhat resembling that of the red-eyed vireo, is an elusive dweller of the swamps and thickets of the Southeastern states, ranging northward to Virginia and westward to the Mississippi. Its large nest of water-soaked leaves is built in canes or shrubs. This warbler is something of an exception in the family since it is, to quote William Brewster, dean of New England ornithology, a "fervent and ecstatic songster," whose ringing whistle is "very loud, very rich, very beautiful, while it has an indescribably tender quality that thrills the senses after the sound has ceased."

The worm-eating warbler, another species that is modestly clad except for its boldly striped head, is also an easterner, with a range extending north to New England and westward almost to the Great Plains. It belongs to a considerable group of warblers that have migratory and possibly ancestral ties with the West Indies rather than with South America. It is a ground-nester, with a gait that is a walk rather than a hop, but it feeds partly in the trees. Its ordinary song resembles the trill of a chipping sparrow or, as some say, a sewing machine!

The *Vermivora* group, represented in America by a dozen forms, is the largest warbler genus after *Dendroica*, the latter having more than thirty. Some species of *Vermivora* are confined to the almost subtropical south, whereas others migrate northward and nest in the Hudsonian or Canadian zones as far as Alaska.

The golden-winged (Plate 147) and blue-winged (Plate 159) warblers breed in overlapping belts in eastern North America, the blue-winged having the more southerly range. This has given rise to a notable case of hybridism, long misunderstood but finally found to fit completely into the hereditary combinations of the Mendelian law. The blue-wing has a yellow breast, green back, a narrow black stripe through the eye, and two white wing bars. The golden-wing has a white breast, a gray back, a broad black stripe through the eye, a black triangle on the throat, and a yellow wing patch. When these two species interbreed, a type formerly called Brewster's warbler is produced. It has the narrow eye stripe of the blue-wing, and the yellow patch and white breast of the golden-wing, but it lacks the black throat

183

mark. Interbreeding among the hybrids, or between a hybrid and one of the parent stocks, produces several genetic types, one of which is the bird originally described as Lawrence's warbler. It inherits the green back, yellow breast, and white wing bars of the blue-wing, but the broad eye stripe and the black triangle of the golden-wing. Lawrence's warbler is statistically much the rarer of the distinct hybrid types, being what geneticists call a "double recessive."

The golden-winged and the blue-winged warblers nest on the ground, or near it, in forest glades or borders, and in old overgrown pastures and orchards. They have indolent, wheezy, buzzing songs, that of the blue-wing usually confined to two syllables, and that of the golden-wing almost invariably more.

Bachman's warbler, a bird of inconspicuous greenish and dull yellow coloring, save for the dark forehead and throat patch of the male, is another inhabitant of Dixie, normally occurring southward from North Carolina and Missouri, and wintering in the West Indies. It is a bird of bottomlands and swampy areas, nesting above the ground, though close to it, in brambles and similar vegetation. It is now considered by many to be the rarest of North American songbirds, and years have passed without a single one being reported.

Its relative, the Tennessee warbler, is of even plainer garb but of quite different habits, for this species winters in Central and South America and is a May migrant, chiefly by way of the Mississippi Valley, to larch and other coniferous forests as far north as Labrador on the east and the upper Yukon Valley on the west. Its spring song, as we have

heard it in the Hudson Valley, is an extraordinarily loud *chipity-chipity-chipity*. Although known to nest on the ground in its northern home, its life history has never yet been adequately studied.

The orange-crowned (Plate 155), lutescent, and dusky warblers are three races of a single species, each in turn occupying more westerly breeding areas. Thus the dusky belongs only to the Santa Catalina and other islands off the coast of California and Lower California, the lutescent warbler is confined to the Pacific Coast of the Northwest, while the orange-crowned is a widespread breeder from Manitoba to Alaska, and a scarce, though regular, migrant in the eastern United States. All three place their nest on or close to the ground; they are hardy in the sense that some of them winter as far north as the southern United States in both the East and the West. A specimen of the orange-crowned has even been collected in Massachusetts in January!

The Nashville warbler (Plate 149) resembles the orange-crowned but is gray-headed, more yellow below, and has a partly concealed chestnut crown, scarcely visible in the field. As a nesting bird it belongs above all to New England, although its range extends from Pennsylvania and New Jersey to Quebec and Saskatchewan. It reaches the United States by a flight across the Gulf of Mexico and is very rare, even as a transient, in the South Atlantic states. Its name arises from the fact that Alexander Wilson first discovered it near Nashville, Tennessee. A similarly casual circumstance accounts for the name of the Tennessee warbler. The Nashville is a bird of birchy uplands and overgrown pastures. If it enters denser tim-

184

ber, it does so to occupy sunny glades. It is a ground-nester and a full-voiced warbler, singing what has been described as a string of eight or more lively, rapid notes, suddenly congested into a pleasant, rolling twitter.

Virginia's warbler and Lucy's warbler (Plate 146), named by their respective discoverers for ladies of their families, are two small western species, prevailingly gray and chestnut-capped in the male. Virginia's has a yellow breast patch and rump, whereas the male of Lucy's warbler has chestnut upper-tail coverts like the crown. Virginia's is a southern Rocky Mountain bird, at home in Colorado and adjacent states and nesting under rocky ledges. Lucy's warbler is of more restricted range, being confined to lower river valleys of the dry country of Utah, New Mexico, Arizona, and southeastern California. It nests behind loose bark, in knot holes, woodpecker cavities, or in the deserted nests of other birds.

The parula warbler (Plate 154) breeds from Florida northward into southern Canada and westward as far as Nebraska. It is an active little bird of many colors—slaty blue, black, white, green, yellow, and a hue close to burnt orange—and it sings a buzzy song on an ascending scale that ends in a veritable explosion. Its song may not be much musically, but it is easy to recognize and is therefore welcome in a family of birds characterized by many vague and readily forgotten vocal efforts.

The uniqueness of the parula centers in its nest, the main structure of which is a long gray-green bag made of Usnea, a hanging tree lichen, in the North, and in the South of the superficially similar Spanish moss,

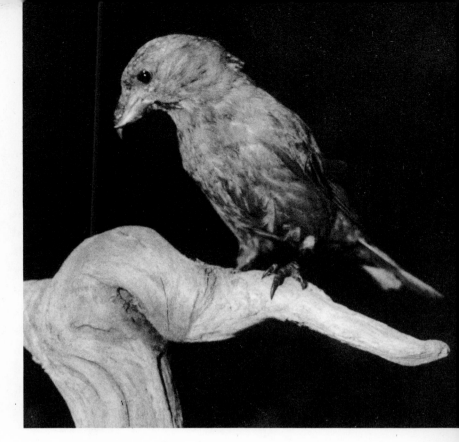

Red Crossbill

which is a relative of the pineapple. Both of these epiphytic plants thrive in moist woodlands, which is therefore the kind of place to seek the parula's nesting site.

Dendroicas or Tree Warblers

The large genus *Dendroica*, which contains a good proportion of the most familiar warblers of the continent, offers many examples of adaptation both in the patterns of plumage and in the way in which these warblers fit into diverse ecological niches.

The yellow warbler is universally known to bird lovers. North America enjoys virtually complete coverage by the species. The male differs from his mate in that the breast and sides are streaked with reddish brown. The forcible and pleasant song of seven or eight syllables, accented on the penultimate, is heard from the bird's arrival in spring

185

until the end of July or into August. One does not need to go to the woods to hear it, for the yellow warblers come to town and city. They build their compact nests in fruit trees or garden shrubs; even in unsettled country this species avoids the deep woods and seeks out such sites as willows along streams. The yellow warbler has acquired fame by its ability to "outwit" the parasitic cowbird. There are countless records of its constructing a new floor over the unwelcome egg laid in its nest. Even three nests, one on top of another, are not uncommon, and instances of four and five are known.

The magnolia warbler (Plate 161) is a gay little picture of clear gray, velvety black, white and yellow, the bijou appearance of the bird being more the result of pattern than of color. Common as a migrant, it breeds in the spruce forests of the northernmost section of the United States and westward into subarctic Canada. At high levels of the Appalachian Mountains the breeding range extends southward as far as Virginia. Although the magnolia warbler flies to the top of tall evergreen trees, its nest is usually in a small fir or spruce, within five or six feet of the ground.

Many regard the Cape May (Plate 143) as the most beautiful of all American warblers. This opinion may be conditioned by the supposed rarity of the bird, but certainly a male Cape May warbler in spring sunshine, with its black crown, bright chestnut ear coverts, yellow neck and nape, black-spotted olive-green back, yellow rump, tiger-striped lower surface, and the fanlike black and white patch on the wings, is a sight not soon to be forgotten. This bird is no longer particularly rare along the Atlantic sea-

board; perhaps its numbers have increased since the time of the early naturalists, when the sight of a Cape May always made a red-letter day. It passes quickly on its way to the north woods, dwelling in Canadian forests from northern New York northward, where it nests in the branches of low evergreens. The Cape May warbler sometimes supplements its diet with the juices of grapes and other fruits. It punctures the fruit with its sharp bill; then its tongue, which is somewhat hollowed out and has a fringe of fine filaments, conveys the juice into the mouth. It also probes wild cherry blossoms, probably to suck up nectar.

It is hard to realize that the black-throated blue warbler is related to such very different-looking species as the magnolia, the Cape May, the cerulean, and the black-poll. Yet, structurally they are all alike, and the females and immatures are none too easy to tell apart. Moreover, the tail quills in most members of *Dendroica* show a curiously common pattern of white inner vanes.

The male black-throated blue (Plate 153) is just that—an exquisite grayish blue, with black face and flanks, white belly, and a small but conspicuous, squarish white spot in the wings. Its usual husky and slow-moving song is easy to recognize. It is of northern or high Appalachian breeding range, but is not confined to coniferous forests, because in the more southerly part it lives among maple, oak, and other hardwoods. Its bulky nest in a fork close to the ground differs from that of other warblers in that rotten wood of a conspicuous light hue ordinarily enters into the outer structure. The interior is neatly lined with grass, fibers, strips of inner bark, fine rootlets, and sometimes porcupine quills.

The big and decorative myrtle warbler (Plate 138) breeds from tree limit in northwestern Alaska eastward and southward to the mountains of New York and Massachusetts. It is a hardy bird in the face of difficult weather, a good proportion of the population wintering in the United States, some as far north as southern New England. Good shelter and a supply of such fruits as those of red cedar, bayberry, and poison ivy determine the distribution, because from a fifth to more than half of its total food supply in winter is made up of plant material. In summer the myrtle is, like other warblers, wholly insectivorous. Analyses of its stomach contents have shown flies, beetles, ants and wasps, aphids, scale insects, caterpillars, moths, and spiders—all indicative of the importance of warblers in maintaining a working balance between vegetation and the small creatures that feed upon it.

The myrtle warbler is always recognizable by the yellow patches on the crown, rump, and sides of breast. If present at all, it is usually abundant. It breeds in coniferous forests, nesting within a few feet of the ground, where the *tchep* call is completely distinctive. Its song is a sprightly "sleighbell" trill.

The Rocky Mountain region accommodates a close cousin of the myrtle, namely Audubon's warbler (Plate 137); in fact, this species has been called the myrtle warbler of the West. It is distinct from the myrtle

Red Crossbills at Nest

in that it has a yellow, instead of a white, throat and more white in wings and tail.

The black-throated gray warbler (Plate 151), another westerner, is colored as its name indicates, except for a tiny yellow spot between the eye and bill. It nests in thin forest with brushy undergrowth, chiefly in dry regions between British Columbia and Lower California.

The black-throated green warbler (Plate 152) is famed for its great range and especially distinctive song. The latter has been put into words as "trees, trees, murmuring trees." The point is that it possesses a pattern and quality that can never be forgotten, whereas, for most people, a certain proportion of the warblers make such elusive or nearly indefinable music that their songs have to be relearned each spring.

The black-throated green frequents coniferous trees. It breeds across Canada, southward to New Jersey, and thence down the Appalachians to Alabama. Although it is generally thought of as a northern warbler, it commonly nests among the red cedars on Long Island. In Massachusetts it is a bird of the white pines, and farther north, of other evergreens. A southern race, the Wayne's warbler, is found in the low cypress country on the coast of South Carolina.

The cerulean warbler stands alone in its light blue plumage. It is a bird of deciduous forests from the Mississippi Valley eastward to the Appalachian Mountains, and it seems to be extending its range toward the coast by way of the Mohawk and Hudson Valleys. Its nest, which resembles that of a flycatcher, is usually placed high on a horizontal or

Brown-capped Rosy Finch at Nest

Evening Grosbeaks

drooping branch. The cerulean warbler is an incessant singer throughout the breeding season.

The attractive, orange-throated Blackburnian warbler (Plate 144), one of the latest spring migrants of the family, travels on to breed in the deep woods of the Canadian zone. Its nest is sometimes built ninety feet or more above the ground, in tall hemlocks or in the largest hardwood trees. Like many other northern warblers, it breeds southward through the mountains to Georgia.

The yellow-throated and sycamore warblers are races of a single species confined respectively to the Southeast and to the area of Mississippi drainage. Both birds are high-nesters, building in sycamores, live oaks, and gum trees.

A few years ago Captain Karl Haller discovered in the foothills of West Virginia a bird, now known as Sutton's warbler, which looks much like a yellow-throated warbler, but which in song and in some details of coloration resembles the parula. Later visitors

189

to this area again observed this puzzling bird. Scientists are still not certain what Sutton's warbler is. That it is a distinct species which escaped detection all these years is difficult to believe. It probably represents a hybrid stock between yellow-throated and parula warblers in which, through continued back-crossing with yellow-throated, the traces of parula blood are now rather well masked. Yet is is hardly likely that two such unlike warblers would cross and produce fertile offspring. Since "normal" yellow-throated (or sycamore) warblers have yet to be found in the area inhabited by Sutton's warbler, it is also possible that the latter is a race of the yellow-throated warbler which *happens* to have a few resemblances to the parula warbler, but this suggestion also strains credulity.

In many parts of central and eastern North America, from the southern Appalachians northward to Canada, the chestnut-sided warbler (Plate 148) is likely to be the most abundant resident woodland bird. It is not a denizen of deep forest but rather of the second growth. When the terrain was largely virgin, Audubon considered the chestnut-side a rare bird, and no doubt its population has doubled and redoubled, like that of robins and certain other species, with the clearing and settlement of the country. It is now almost a rival of the yellow warbler in its close association with man. The nests and even the songs of the two are also rather similar.

The bay-breasted warbler, whose male displays a rich chestnut or bay-colored crown and breast, is one of the rarer species in the middle latitudes, although at times it comes in large migratory flights. In the morning after such a nocturnal arrival, the trees and shrubs, and even suburban lawns, may be full of bay-breasts. On the ground they remind one of tiny, richly hued robins.

Rock Sparrow

Tree Sparrow

Their stay is brief, for they go on to nest in the zone of hemlocks and other evergreens that stretches from northeastern New England and the Adirondack Mountains westward to Manitoba. The bay-breasted is a weak-voiced warbler, its notes being liquid and inarticulate.

The genetic kinship of many different-looking warblers of the genus *Dendroica*, to which reference has already been made, is especially well illustrated by the autumn female, and particularly the young, of the black-poll warbler, which closely resembles the bay-breasted in similar stages. The spring male plumages of the two are, however, totally unlike. The black-poll is a late migrant, and it lingers long on its way north. Its spring call, *east, east, east, east,* uttered with a rising inflection, is one of the last utterances of the transient spring birds to reach human ears. Some black-polls do go east, to Maine and elsewhere, but others move northwestward as far as Alaska. The normal wintering area extends into South America as far as Brazil, and examples have even been collected as far south as Chile. The black-poll is one of the few warblers to migrate directly across the West Indies from Venezuela to Florida. It has been said that no black-poll has a one-way migration trek

191

of less than twenty-five hundred miles and that, in the case of many members of the species, the annual round trip exceeds ten thousand miles.

The pine warbler is a greenish bird, somewhat brighter below, and inclined to be — or at least to look — rather resinous and sticky with pine sap. Even the whitish wing bars have a dingy appearance. Except at some of the stations of its migratory trips, it spends its life in pines, in which it nests. Pine seeds and other vegetable foods are included in its diet, although, like other warblers, it lives mostly on insects. There are two races of this species, one of them confined to southern Florida and the keys. The other ranges northward into Canada, and its mellow, trilling song is characteristic of such places as the pitch-pine barrens of New Jersey, Long Island, and Cape Cod.

Another piny warbler, and the largest member of the *Dendroica* group in size, although smallest in numbers, is Kirtland's warbler (Plate 142), which breeds in three counties of the state of Michigan, and nowhere else. It winters only in the Bahama Islands. Its nesting range is determined by the presence of young jack pines which are growing in burned-over areas. As soon as the pines exceed a height of eight feet or so, the warblers depart in search of another similar area. Its total population has now been estimated at less than one thousand birds, and it is accounted one of the rarest of all the wood warblers.

The prairie warbler (Plate 140) has a simple song of rising phrases of rare musical quality, notwithstanding the fact that Dr. Elliott Coues has likened it to the plaint of a mouse with a toothache! It is a yellow and green little bird, spotted with black on face and flanks, and flecked with reddish tint on the back. It lives and nests in scrubby pastures and low second growth from the Mississippi Valley to the Atlantic Coast and from Florida to Ontario.

The last members of *Dendroica* are the palm warblers, of which the two races — the western and the yellow — differ enough in color so that a trained observer can distinguish them in life. Both forms breed almost wholly north of the United States and both nest on the ground in moss or sphagnum under coniferous forests. Except for Kirtland's warbler, they are the only typical ground-nesters in the genus. The palm warblers are modestly colored birds with reddish brown crowns. Their incessant tail wagging helps to identify them.

Ground Warblers

The ovenbird and the water-thrushes make up another group of warblers. All have fine capabilities as songsters, and all nest on the ground. The ovenbird (Plate 165), which resides in rich woodlands northward to Newfoundland, takes its name from the fancied resemblance of its nest to an outdoor Dutch oven. It is best known from its crescendo *teacher* call, but it also has a lively, warbling flight song, usually rendered at night during the courtship season.

The northern water-thrush (Plate 163) is a warbler of bogs, forest swamps, and lake shores, chiefly north of the United States. It eats many kinds of aquatic organisms in

(Continued on page 209)

192

187 *Cardinal. A resident wherever found, the cardinal is less common in the North.*

188

White-winged Crossbill. An erratic wanderer in winter.

189

*Lawrence's Goldfinch. Nests only in California but
is found in Arizona during the winter.
Several pairs may nest in one tree.*

House Finch. Its call notes resemble those of house sparrows but it also has a warbling song.

190

191

American Goldfinch. One of the most abundant species of eastern North America. It feeds on weed seeds beside the road and flies up, twittering, when a human being approaches. Several of its notes are very plaintive.

Arkansas Goldfinch. Also known as the green-backed goldfinch, this bird is common in Mexico as well as in our West. Like other goldfinches, it nests late in the season.

192

193

*Rose-breasted Grosbeak. The male is one of the
handsomest of summer birds; the streaked
female and young resemble large sparrows.*

*Evening Grosbeak. A glance at its heavy bill reveals the origin of the name
"grosbeak." It can crack the hardest seeds and extract the kernels.*

194

195 *Blue Grosbeak. Differs from the indigo bunting in larger size and heavier bill.*

196

Black-headed Grosbeak. A western rose-breasted grosbeak.

197

*Pyrrhuloxia. Perhaps because it is seen only along our southwestern borders
this striking bird has never acquired a common name.*

198

*Pink-sided Junco. Nests in
Saskatchewan, Wyoming, and
Idaho; related forms inhabit
adjacent states.*

199

Gray-headed Junco. Like other juncos it may be recognized by white outer tail feathers, tinkling song, and characteristic flock note.

Slate-colored Junco. Also called common snow bird, in winter it is often seen in back yards.

200

201

Pine Siskin. Sometimes found in hemlock woods in flocks of hundreds. In flight and voice it resembles the common goldfinch.

Red-eyed Towhee. Generally found in dry, brushy pastures and barrens. In the Southeast this race gives way to the white-eyed towhee.

202

203

Spotted Towhee. A somewhat shyer bird than the eastern towhee. Its call note resembles that of the catbird.

Spotted Towhee. Usually builds its nest on the ground and often rears two broods in succession. Three eggs are the normal clutch.

204

205

Abert's Towhee. A very shy southwestern species; even when its nest has been discovered it usually remains hidden, protesting from a distance.

Brown Towhee. Seen from California to Mexico City. Race shown here is Arizona "canyon towhee."

206

207

Chipping Sparrow. The "chippy" likes horsehair for its nest; today it often uses substitutes.

208
Song Sparrow. Each male of this group has a variety of songs and switches constantly from one to another.

209

Black-throated Sparrow. Also known as the desert sparrow, this is one of the most attractive and common birds of our southwestern deserts.

210

Fox Sparrow. A large, handsome sparrow of the same hue as a red fox. It has a melodious song.

211

Field Sparrow. An eastern species and a fine songster. Recognized by its pinkish bill.

212

White-crowned Sparrow. Known only as a migrant in the East. The western races nest from Alaska to as far south as California.

White-crowned Sparrow. A large sparrow with a modest but very pleasing color pattern.

213

214

Golden-crowned Sparrow. A little-known bird. In winter it mingles with the more common western white-crowned sparrows.

215

Vesper Sparrow. As the name implies, its song is usually uttered toward nightfall, when the bird is perched on a fencepost or boulder.

White-throated Sparrow. A clear metallic call note announces this migrant.

216

217

Lark Sparrow. Found primarily in open country in the West, this sparrow may wander as far east as Maine but does not nest there.

218

Clay-colored Sparrow. An obscurely colored cousin of the familiar chipping sparrow; it nests in the North Central States as far east as Michigan.

219

Olive Sparrow. Nests in thorny desert plants.

220

Snow Bunting. In winter large flocks hunt for weed seeds.

Tree Sparrow. A misleading name for a winter visitor that lives in weedy fields.

221

addition to insects, and on its migrations it sometimes visits tidal sand bars, where it associates with shore birds.

The Louisiana water-thrush (Plate 162) is a paler and larger species and a familiar resident of woodland brook courses throughout much of the eastern half of the United States and Canada. The "thrush" part of the name comes, of course, from the spotted breast, which is shared by the ovenbird.

The Connecticut warbler and its relatives make up a small group, of which the Kentucky warbler (Plate 139), which breeds from the Hudson Valley westward to Nebraska and southward to Louisiana, is the most distinctive in appearance. The male has a broad black mark below the eye, and in both sexes the eye is surrounded by a yellow loop running backward from the bill. The species dwells as close to New York City as the woods of the Hudson River Palisades. It nests on or just off the ground and is a loud and persistent singer.

The males of two other members of this group wear gray hoods over the entire head, the remainder of the plumage being greenish above and yellow below. They are more northerly than the Kentucky warbler and both nest on or near the ground in shrubs or grassy areas of relatively high latitudes. The Connecticut warbler, which has a conspicuous white eye ring, has little to do with Connecticut, except as a none too common autumn migrant. Its summer home is in northern tamarack swamps. The mourning warbler (Plate 141) lacks the eye ring of the Connecticut and has a black bib on the pectoral part of its gray hood. Another member, Macgillivray's warbler, combines the black bib markings with an eye ring interrupted both front and rear, and breeds in the West northward into arctic Alaska.

The common yellow-throat (Plate 164) is a species with numerous forms which pretty well cover North America northward to Newfoundland, Labrador, Vancouver Island, and even Alaska. They nest in hummocks or other dense growths on or close to the ground and are usually associated with marshes and other damp places, although bramble patches and the tangles of old fields will serve. Yellow-throats sing a simple song, which can be rendered as *witchity-witchity-witchity*.

The males have a black band of color across their eyes all year — which led the children of one of the authors to invent their own name for this bird — "bandit warbler." Behind the mask, or above it, a whitish stripe crosses the head, and for some unknown reason this usually runs askew, so that the two sides of the plumage pattern are not quite symmetrical. This is a rare phenomenon among vertebrates, most of which are bilateral even down to minor details.

The chats are somewhat anomalous wood warblers because of their large size (almost equal to that of a catbird), heavy bills, and generally unwarblerlike behavior. In structure, pattern, and in the selection of habitat, however, they show kinship with the yellow-throat group.

The yellow-breasted chat (Plate 166), which has a tremendous vocabulary and which even seems to be more or less of a mimic, resides throughout most of temperate North America westward to the Great Plains. It is a bird of tangles and thickets, at once shy, suspicious, elusive, and yet very curious. It is heard, however, much more often than it is seen. It eats many ground beetles and weevils, as well as grasshoppers and true bugs, and varies its insect diet with such fleshy fruits as blackberries, blueberries, elderberries, pokeweed, and the fruits of sumac, dogwood, and nightshade.

Fly-catching Warblers

Among the fly-catching group is the lovely hooded warbler (Plate 145), in which the male has a bright yellow mask on its otherwise black hood. It is a bird of damp deciduous forests with rich undergrowth and is found in localities suitable to it all over the eastern half of the United States from southern New England and Nebraska southward to the Gulf. It nests and lives close to the ground, but not on it. The song has been described by the sentence, "You must come to the woods or you won't see me."

Wilson's warbler (Plate 158), a greenish and yellow sprite, with a pert black cap in the male, is a ground-nesting northern species. It was named for the pioneer American ornithologist, Alexander Wilson, who discovered and described no fewer than eleven American warblers.

The Canada warbler (Plate 156), a graybacked bird that wears a charming necklace of black dots across the yellow breast, is a common late spring migrant throughout the eastern United States. It breeds from Connecticut northward to eastern and central Canada, nesting on the ground or in a decayed stump or fern clump in damp woodlands. Both the Canada and the Wilson's warbler are agile at catching insects in the

air, paralleling the well-developed fly-catching propensities of the redstart.

The redstart (Plate 157), in which the adult male is instantly recognizable because of the combination of black and salmon color in its gay plumage, breeds over much of North America westward to the Rocky Mountains. Female and young birds have a plumage pattern similar to that of the male, but gray-green replaces the black, and pale yellow the salmon. Young males assume the adult plumage only in their second year.

This is the friskiest of all wood warblers. It flits rapidly through deciduous trees of open second-growth stands or bottomlands, fanning out its long and conspicuous tail and frequently allowing the wings to droop. From time to time it darts into the air to catch an insect. No doubt the well-developed bristles around its bill are an aid in this performance, for they are similar to those of many true flycatchers. Its neat nest is usually built in an upright crotch of a shrub or small tree. The redstart is vocally very versatile, some of its songs resembling those of the chestnut-sided warbler, except that the stressed note is usually the final one.

The painted redstart, of southern mountain ranges in Arizona and New Mexico, is even gaudier. There is, indeed, nothing else like it in this family of birds, for the breast and belly are scarlet, the upper surface shiny black, and the sides of the tail broadly white. Even more remarkable is the fact that females wear the same brilliant garb as their mates, and the young come right into adult plumage from the nestling stage. The painted redstart nests on the ground, sometimes under a projecting rock on a slope, and preferably near running or falling water. One of the most astonishing examples of the wanderings of birds was the recent appearance of a painted redstart on Cape Cod.

Blackbirds and Orioles   28

Blackbirds, grackles, cowbirds, orioles, meadowlarks and bobolinks—all are members of the American blackbird and oriole family—although they differ greatly in appearance and in habits. Most of them are rather heavy-billed birds that feed on seeds, including cultivated grains. Orioles, however, are insectivorous and some of them have thinner bills for securing nectar and small insects from flowers. The meadowlark has a straight, pointed bill with which it can probe the ground for grubs. In this it resembles the starlings of the Old World, and early naturalists thought that blackbirds were related to starlings. A resemblance in color between the New and Old World orioles is also evident but is only skin-deep. The true relationship of the American orioles and blackbirds seems to be not with the Old World starlings or orioles but with the finch family. Indeed, the cowbird is an example of a heavy-billed bird that is very much like the finches.

The orioles are best known for their finely woven hanging nests. The crow-sized tropical orioles, known as oropendolas, construct swinging nests that are a yard long. Grackles build simple open nests in trees, as do the meadowlarks and bobolinks on the ground. And, finally, the cowbird slyly lays its egg in the nests of other birds and leaves them to hatch and rear its young. The red-winged blackbird supplies a transition between the specialized nests of the orioles and the simple efforts of the grackles and bobolinks. It supports its nest-cup among reeds by twisting strands around the stems as might an apprentice oriole.

In voice, too, the members of this group show great variations. The bubbling song of the handsome bobolink is, in its way, unsurpassed among birds, but the best efforts of its relatives, the grackles and cowbirds, are discordant squawks and whistles.

In this family, the male is usually more brightly colored and also larger than his mate or mates. In many species, such as the cowbird and the boat-tailed grackle, the male performs grotesque antics as he displays his shiny iridescent black plumes and brings forth, as though with great physical effort, his whistled and piping courtship cries. Some of the tropical oropendolas lean far forward and almost fall from the perch while uttering what can only be called a ludicrous gurgle.

Orioles

The Baltimore oriole (Plate 178) is widely distributed and well known in the northeastern and central United States. It commonly selects the long drooping terminal twigs of the American elm as the site for its hanging nests. Year after year a pair of orioles will nest in the same elm beside some old farmhouse along a country road. Fine plant fibers are used in weaving the nest, which is constructed entirely by the female, while her handsome mate sings and displays in the nearby trees. Sometimes an oriole accidentally loops a noose of fiber or string around its head while building its nest and thus hangs itself.

In their snug deep nest, young orioles are secure from most enemies. Though windstorms may swing the nest to and fro, they rarely blow it down. Perhaps because they are so well protected from cats and other enemies, young orioles are very noisy in begging their parents for food. Even after they leave the nest, their loud insistent chirping may be heard as long as they can induce the old birds to feed them.

The loud, clear, whistled song of the Baltimore Oriole may be heard throughout the early portion of the summer and again briefly in September, before it migrates south to its winter home, which extends from southern Mexico to Colombia, South America. Its orange and black were the colors of Lord Baltimore, first Governor of Maryland, which explains its name.

The white-shouldered Bullock's oriole (Plate 175) of the West is a close relative of the Baltimore oriole; the two species sometimes interbreed in Oklahoma, where their ranges meet. The orchard oriole (Plate 174) is found in the Southeastern states and westward into Texas and Mexico. Its nest is less skillfully woven than that of the Baltimore oriole. The male is black and burnt orange; the female is olive green. This oriole migrates south very early, and migrants appear in Mexico as early as July.

The remaining orioles of the United States barely cross the southwestern border. The beautiful hooded oriole (Plate 177) cradles its nest in a palm leaf. Scott's oriole (Plate 176), a handsome lemon-yellow species, inhabits the arid hillsides of Arizona, where it nests among the picturesque yuccas or century plants. The Audubon's or black-throated oriole enters the United States in southern Texas. Recently one of the authors, encamped with a group on the banks of the Rio Sabinas in the southern part of the Mexican state of Tamaulipas, observed that a clump of moss on the lower limbs of a huge water cypress held a nest of the Audubon's oriole. Both parents were most industrious in bringing food to the nest; neither the constant rain nor the generally gloomy weather interrupted their work. What was the amazement of the campers when they found that the sole inmate of the nest was an oversized, voracious young red-eyed cowbird, which had undoubtedly crowded the young orioles out of their home.

Cowbirds, too, as already noted, are members of the oriole family. The red-eyed cowbird, mentioned above, is found only in the southwestern United States and in Mexico. Better known is the widely distributed common or brown-headed cowbird (Plate 167). The ability of this parasite to locate the nests of other birds is phenomenal. In some areas almost every nest of song sparrow, red-eyed vireo, and ovenbird contains a cowbird egg. The female cowbird finds nests by watching the proposed victims building; then, after the nest is finished, she slips into it early one morning and lays one of her eggs. She may, at the same time, or a day before, carry off one of the eggs of the rightful owner of the nest, thereby making the competition for her own young less severe. Usually, the cowbird lays her egg in the nests of smaller species. The egg hatches after only twelve days of incubation, a day or two less than is required by the eggs of most of the species that are parasitized. The young cowbird has every advantage, and usually the other youngsters do not survive.

Normally the cowbird does not lay more than one of her own eggs in the same nest, but sometimes different cowbirds parasitize the same victim, and nests of vireos and other species containing two or three cowbird eggs are not uncommon. A few species of birds, of which the robin is one, will not tolerate the activities of the cowbird. They remove the alien egg or abandon the nest. Most birds, however, do not seem to take note of the strange egg, and faithfully care for it and later for the young cowbird.

For a brief period after leaving the nest, young cowbirds follow their foster parents, begging incessantly. At such times, one often observes a pair of little warblers striving to satisfy the gross appetites of an infant twice their size. A week or two later, the young cowbird, with a sure, instinctive recognition of its species, joins other cowbirds. These flocks seek the vicinity of cows (as in former days they sought bison), where they walk and flutter about fearlessly, feeding upon insects disturbed by the grazing animals.

Blackbirds

Best known of American blackbirds is the common redwing (Plate 172). It is a bird of marshes, but any damp meadow or swale is sufficient for its needs. The shiny black male,

with his glistening red shoulder patches or epaulets, puffs himself out in the spring sunshine and utters a loud *kong-ka-ree.* His mate is a smaller and more modestly dressed bird of streaked gray and whitish plumage. The male redwing, like most other songbirds, sets up an area or territory from which he drives other males. The territory of such redwings is extremely well defined, as though an actual fence existed around each domain. Frequently a male succeeds in attracting two mates to his area. Occasionally the redwings leave the nesting territory and fly away to feed on neutral ground.

Both the large yellow-headed blackbird (Plate 171) and the shiny black Brewer's blackbird (Plate 173) are found in the West. The former lives in colonies in the reeds or tules that border lakes and marshes; the latter, one of the commonest blackbirds, builds a cup-shaped nest in a crotch of a pine tree. The rusty blackbird of the East is closely related but less well known because it nests in the spruce woods of Maine and eastern Canada. Its conspicuous white eye helps identify it.

The common grackle, of which the bronzed and the purple grackles are varieties, is an abundant bird in eastern North America. Viewed in the sun, its plumage sparkles with metallic luster. The long tail, which is slightly keeled or ridged, accounts for about half of its length. The male grackle is a pompous creature and struts before his mate uttering harsh notes that have been compared with the squeaking of a rusty gate. Grackles love to nest in evergreens beside houses or in parks or cemeteries. In the autumn they join redwings, cowbirds, and starlings in huge night roosts.

Such assemblages produce a tremendous din, and when the roost is near residences great efforts are made to induce the birds to move elsewhere.

The boat-tailed grackle (Plate 168) of the South Atlantic states and Gulf Coast is a larger edition of the common grackle. The female is much smaller than the male and is brownish black, while her mate is a brilliant iridescent black. In the Southeast the boat-tailed grackle is very much of a colonial marsh bird, but on the coast of Texas and in Mexico it is a common bird around villages and ranches.

Meadowlarks and Bobolinks

Meadowlarks are grassland birds with beautiful yellow breasts and streaked plumage. In earlier times they were hunted as game birds, but they are, to use an old phrase, indifferent tablebirds but notable soloists, and should be protected. Meadowlarks have the habit of nervously flicking their white outer tail feathers as they utter sputtering alarm notes. The eastern meadowlark (Plate 170) can scarcely be told from the western species except by the expert with specimens at hand, but the song of the western bird is much more musical.

Although related to the blackbirds and orioles, the bobolink (Plate 169) is in a class by itself. The female is a plainly colored sparrowlike bird, identified by the pointed tail feathers plainly visible in the photograph. The male is a handsome black, white, and buff creature. He is a wonderful songster, and gives his ringing melody as he hovers on quivering wings above his mate lying hidden in the meadow below. After the nesting season, the male bobolink abruptly acquires a streaked protective coloration like that of his mate and both set off on their long migration, which takes them as far as the grasslands of Argentina. As they pass overhead on their night migration, the metallic call note is easily recognized.

Years ago, when rice was an important crop in the South Carolina lowlands, bobolinks stopped there each fall to feed upon the ripening grain. So well developed was this habit that they became known as rice birds. Now that the center of rice culture in the United States has shifted to the West, outside the main migratory paths, the southern rice fields are no longer visited by great flocks of these birds.

Tanagers   29

Tanagers are brilliantly colored birds native to the American tropics. Related to finches, they differ from them in that their food is chiefly fruit and insects, not seeds. Of the approximately two hundred species of tanagers, only four reach the United States: the scarlet tanager in the East, the western or Louisiana tanager in the West, the summer tanager in the South, and the hepatic tanager in the Southwest.

The male scarlet tanager (Plates 179, 181), flaming red with black wings and tail, is the most brilliant summer bird of eastern

North America. Although common, it remains within the shade of large groves of trees where the casual passer-by rarely sees it. The naturalist quickly learns its song, which is like that of the American robin, but uttered more rapidly. The call note is very distinctive—a two-syllabled *chip-churr*, the second note having a twangy quality like the plucking of a guitar string.

The female tanager is a plain, greenish bird, and to this more protective coloration the male also changes before the southward migration to the winter home in South America. The nest of the scarlet tanager is a cup of twigs lined with black rootlets.

The western tanager (Plate 180) is closely related to the scarlet tanager, although the male is quite different in coloration. In the summer tanager (Plate 182) of the South, the male is uniformly rosy red. His song is more melodious than that of the other tanagers. This species is common in the Southeast and occurs locally in the Southwest, where the resident race is known as Cooper's tanager.

The hepatic (liver-colored) tanager is another species in which the mature male is entirely red. This is a Mexican bird which barely enters the limits of the United States.

Finches, Cardinals, and Sparrows 30

Inasmuch as sixty or more species of this, the largest family of songbirds, nest in the United States, the following survey can do no more than discuss some of the more interesting ones. Finches have a heavy, conical bill used to crush seeds, which form a large part of their food. They are favorite cage birds, for they are pretty and sing well. Because of their diet of seeds they are easy to keep. Colorful American finches, such as the painted bunting and the cardinal, can no longer be legally kept in cages, but some of the Old World finches are still to be seen in pet shops. The canary is, of course, by all odds the commonest of caged finches. Pet fanciers call finches "hardbills," while insect-eating songbirds, such as thrushes, are called "softbills."

The Cardinal Group

The brilliant cardinal (Plate 187) and its southwestern relative the pyrrhuloxia (Plate 197) form the nucleus of a group of finches of southern origin. Most of them, such as the rose-breasted grosbeak (Plate 193) and the indigo bunting (Plates 183, 184) are migratory. Insects rather than seeds form the principal part of their diet, at least at certain seasons. The cardinal itself, however, is somewhat of an exception, and more like other finches in that it is nonmigratory and has a powerful bill, which it uses to crack seeds. In the northern part of its range it often lends a brilliant bit of color to the winter landscape, and for this reason is a favorite with designers of Christmas cards.

The cardinal feeds insects to its young until they are old enough to begin eating seeds. Dr. J. Van Tyne thus describes an amusing incident that occurred while he was watching a pair of cardinals with young:

"The adult male, on his way back to the nest territory, stopped at my feeding shelf with his beak full of small green worms such as I had often seen him feed to the young. He immediately put the worms down on the shelf and began cracking and eating sunflower seeds. After a minute or two he took the worms in his beak but again laid them down and ate a few more seeds. He then picked up the worms for the second time, flew across the street, and (presumably) fed the young."

The singing abilities of the finches of the cardinal group differ considerably. The cardinal has a loud but rather unvaried song. The rich warbling song of the rose-breasted grosbeak places it in the first rank of American songbirds; its song is similar to that of the robin, but richer and more musical. The indigo bunting also has a warbling song, but somewhat inferior in quality to that of the rose-breasted grosbeak. This bunting sings with great persistence through the long hot days of midsummer.

The black-headed grosbeak (Plate 196) of the West is related to the rose-breasted grosbeak of the East, while the lazuli bunting (Plate 186) in the West takes the place of its cousin, the eastern indigo bunting. In both instances the eastern bird happens to be more beautiful than the related western one. On the other hand, the cardinals of the Southwest are, if anything, even more colorful than those of the East.

The blue grosbeak of the Southern states is like a large edition of the indigo bunting, with which it is often confused, but its

heavy bill and rusty shoulder patches distinguish it from the smaller bird.

The Goldfinch Group

To this clan belong the goldfinches and their European relative, the canary, as well as the purple and house finches, the crossbills, the evening and pine grosbeaks, the siskins, and the rosy finches of the Rockies. The northern finches, such as the crossbills, feed chiefly upon the seeds of various evergreens, which they extract skillfully from the cones. The abundance of cones varies from year to year, and in winters of scarcity north of the border, these colorful finches visit the United States to the delight of birders. At such times the black and yellow evening grosbeaks (Plate 194) flock about suburban feeding stations, while the curious white-winged crossbills (Plate 188) may be closely approached and even picked up by hand, so tame are they, as they busily feed on the cones of hemlocks.

The hard seeds which these finches crush in their thick bills are too coarse for the newly hatched young. For them the seeds are swallowed and predigested in the crop of the parent, and then regurgitated into the mouths of the young. The most unusual feeding adaptation is found in the crossbills: the crossed tips of the bill of these birds are inserted between the scales of a pine cone to pry them apart and expose the edible seeds. Perhaps the most powerful bill is possessed by the stocky evening grosbeak. This handsome bird is very fond of sunflower seeds and comes readily to feeding stations to obtain them.

The goldfinches and purple finches are more southern in their distribution, reaching South America. One South American species, the hooded siskin, is of interest because fanciers are crossing it with canaries in an attempt to produce new color varieties. The red and orange pigments of finches are rather sensitive to environmental influences and often disappear in captivity. The rose-colored house finch (Plate 190) of California was introduced into the Hawaiian Islands where, perhaps because of the moist climate, the prevailing color of the birds became yellow instead of red. This finch has also been introduced and is now established on Long Island, New York.

The Western states are the home of two species of goldfinches, the Arkansas or green-backed goldfinch (Plate 192), and the Lawrence's goldfinch (Plate 189). The latter has one of the smallest distributions of any of our birds. Southern California comprises its summer range, while in winter it migrates east rather than south and sometimes appears in Arizona.

The pine siskin (Plate 201) is a rather inconspicuous finch, best told by its twangy call notes and the slightly forked yellow and gray tail. It is common in the western mountains south even into Mexico but in the East is more northerly and is usually seen in the winter or spring, when flocks often appear in hemlock woods.

Goldfinches are often called wild canaries, but the true ancestor of the domestic canary is an Old World bird native to the Canary Islands and to the countries along the Mediterranean. The wild birds are greenish yellow, streaked with gray and hence rather inconspicuous. The beautiful pure yellow of the pet male canary is a result of man's care and selection. Many breeds of canaries now exist, some valued for their beauty and gracefulness, others for their sweet songs. The best singers belong to a strain of birds developed in the Harz Mountains of Germany. Great attention is given to their training. The young birds are placed with an old one that is known to be a good singer, and the former learn to sing by imitating the "teacher." Many wild finches sing almost as well as the trained canary. The purple finch, the house finch, and the American goldfinch (Plate 191), whose ecstatic song is uttered as it flies slowly on trembling wings near its nesting place, are all excellent songsters.

The Native Sparrows

The numerous species known in America as sparrows and in Europe as buntings form the third main group of the large finch family. Sparrows are more modestly colored than the finches of the cardinal and goldfinch tribes, but on close examination their plumage pattern is found to be intricate and harmonious. They often live in grassy fields and are streaked to resemble their environment. The native sparrows feed upon seeds or insects, according to the season.

The best-known of this group is the song sparrow (Plate 208) which ranges over much of the continent, including even the bleak Aleutian Islands, where a resident race searches for its food among the storm-tossed wrack on the beaches. The cheerful song of this sparrow is heard even in stormy or cold weather; thus its name was acquired. The larger chestnut-colored fox sparrow (Plate 210) is closely related to the song sparrow but is of northerly distribution.

A kindred tribe is that containing the white-crowned (Plates 212, 213) and white-throated sparrows (Plate 216). These large handsome sparrows nest, for the most part, north of the American borders, but are commonly seen during migration and, in the South, throughout the winter. The late S. Prentice Baldwin, pioneer bird bander, found that ringed white-throated sparrows returned each winter to his garden in Thomasville, Georgia; they were as true to their winter quarters as to their nesting home. The plaintive, piping song of the white-throat is among the sweetest bird songs of the Canadian woods.

The white-crowned sparrow is of more northern distribution than the white-throat, at least in the East. In the winter vast numbers of these sparrows flock into northwestern Mexico where on sunny days they assemble in brush piles and sing softly. A little farther north, in California, the flocks of wintering white-crowns sometimes contain a few individuals of the golden-crowned sparrow (Plate 214), a migrant from Alaska and one of the least known of American finches.

The little chipping sparrow (Plate 207) is one of the familiar dooryard birds of the East. Its confiding habits make it easier to identify than some of its western cousins, such as the clay-colored sparrow (Plate 218), particularly since the chippy, as it is called, has a chestnut crown patch and conspicuous white lines above the eye. It nests in arbors and hedgerows, where it

makes a cuplike nest lined with horsehair. Its song is a trill of chirps completely devoid of inflection. Much more melodious is the song of its cousin, the field sparrow (Plate 211). This bird lives in dry brushy pastures and fields where it is supplanted in the winter by a hardy and charming species from the North—the misnamed tree sparrow (Plate 221). One windy winter day, the authors paused to watch a flock of these birds that had gathered in some tall weeds protruding above the snow. As the birds hopped about in search of seeds, they uttered soft warbling notes, sometimes perching on the weed stalks to feed directly from the plants. When a rabbit hunter in a distant woods fired his gun, the birds fluttered into the gnarled limbs of an old apple tree, but in a few moments dropped to the ground again to resume feeding. Such small birds must feed busily throughout winter days in order to survive the long cold nights.

In eastern hayfields one finds the inconspicuous savannah sparrow and the grasshopper sparrow, so called from its thin, sibilant, insectlike song. On fallow overgrown fields, the curious little Henslow's sparrow attracts attention by its two-syllabled clicking song, while the vesper sparrow (Plate 215), with its white outer tail feathers, often flies out from underfoot as one steps near its hidden nest. The identification of all these sparrows presents a problem, and a good pair of binoculars is necessary equipment. Once learned, the song of each of these is distinctive. The lark sparrow (Plate 217) is larger and more clearly marked than the other grassland species.

The juncos, or snowbirds, are distinguished by white outer tail feathers and gray breast. Juncos appear in the Northern states in the late fall and stay throughout the winter. The slate-colored junco (Plate 200) is the eastern species; several others, including the pink-sided and gray-headed juncos (Plates 198, 199), are found in the western mountains.

The towhees are among the largest of the sparrows. The red-eyed towhee (Plate 202) of the East and the spotted towhee (Plates 203, 204) of the West are closely related, as are the brown (Plate 206) and the Abert's towhees (Plate 205) of the Southwest. They are all birds of brushy places, more often heard than seen. In addition to the ringing whistled call *to-whee* from which it receives its name, the red-eyed towhee has an attractive song which it utters from the top of a low tree or bush. Also called the ground robin and the chewink, the male is a handsome black, white, and chestnut bird. Like the fox sparrow, it scratches noisily among dry leaves to uncover insects and seeds.

The longspurs and snow buntings (Plate 220) of the arctic tundra are also members of this group. In winter large restless flocks of these birds visit the Northern states, where they sweep about over the snowy landscape in search of weed seeds.

The lark bunting, which nests on the high plateaus of Wyoming, winters in northern Mexico. The male is a handsome black and white creature, a little like a bobolink, but the female, and for that matter the male in winter plumage, is streaked with dusky gray and brown, like the individual shown in Plate 185.

Among the other members of the sparrow tribe are several that are at home in the deserts of the Southwest. Two of these are the olive or Texas sparrow (Plate 219) and the desert or black-throated sparrow (Plate 209). The desert sparrow seems to think arid wastes quite the best places in the world so long as there are a few thorny bushes in which it can perch to sing. The olive sparrow is of much the same persuasion, but enemies do exist in its desert home. Attracted by the frenzied chipping of a pair of these birds while in Mexico, the authors found that a snake was robbing their nest, even though it was situated in the very center of a massive clump of organ-pipe cactus. Falling to with a machete, we succeeded in hacking away the outer stems of the cactus and securing the snake, but not before it had emptied the nest of young birds.

House or English Sparrows

This bird, which was introduced from Europe to America in 1850, has now spread from the Atlantic to the Pacific. Along with the pigeon, it is very well known to the city dweller. It is often regarded with some affection, even though it is a noisy, quarrelsome rowdy which may drive martins and other desirable birds from their nesting places.

The house sparrow belongs to an Old World family known as weaver finches. They are especially numerous in Africa and Australia. With the exception of the canary, most small finches sold as cagebirds belong to this family. As the name "weaver finch" suggests, many members of this family weave hanging nests. In this respect, as in others, the house sparrow is hardly a credit to the family, with its untidy, feather-lined nest placed in the cranny of a building.

219

Sometimes it may, among the twigs of a tree, build a rounded nest with a side entrance, but even these are not things of beauty.

Brood after brood of young sparrows are raised during the summer. Like their mother, the young birds of both sexes are plain grayish brown. In time the males acquire a black bib and chestnut ear patches. Though not unattractive, their plumage becomes so dingy as a result of feeding and roosting in dirty places that the true color is almost concealed.

Notes on Bird Photography

by ELIOT PORTER

SUCCESSFUL BIRD photography depends on three factors: a knowledge of bird habits sufficient to find the birds one wishes to photograph, the ability to use the most modern photographic equipment, and an appreciation of the creative possibilities of photography.

Knowledge of the habits and behavior of birds can be acquired as one goes along, but initial success will come faster if one has made some preliminary study of the subject. For example, a great deal of time might be wasted by a novice looking for the nest of a migrant bird in the spring. It is also important to be able to identify, by appearance and calls, the birds of the region in which one is working, to know the differences between males and females, and to be able to interpret their behavior. Anyone who spends much time in the field has an unparalleled opportunity to add to his knowledge of birds and thereby increase his effectiveness as a photographer.

Once the bird is located, photographing it is largely a technical problem whose solution depends on the kind of bird, the time of year, and the place where the bird is found. The methods available for photographing a hummingbird differ from those for photographing a hawk; and a bird at its nest cannot be photographed in quite the same way as at a feeding station in winter. The fundamental problem in all cases is to find a place to which the bird is likely to return, primarily the nest. Other places include established feeding stations and bird baths, and natural locations habitually visited by certain species: a trumpet vine frequented by hummingbirds or a shore line by wading birds.

Some birds are photographed most easily from a blind and with a reflex camera equipped with a telephoto or long-focus lens. But a telephoto lens should be used only when it is not possible to get a large image with other lenses; it is useful, for example, in photographing shore birds at the water's edge, or hawks whose nests are not too high or shaded by foliage. By means of this lens very beautiful photographs can be made of large birds as they circle over and approach their nests.

With the great majority of small birds it is practical to use flash photography because the light output from an artificial source can be concentrated to give an illumination many times brighter than that of the sun. With larger birds the light must be distributed over a wider area, thus reducing the advantage of artificial illumination. Flash photography permits the use of shutter speeds and lens apertures not otherwise possible. The faster the shutter the more motion the photograph will arrest, and the smaller the stop the greater the depth of focus and over-all sharpness of the image. Both these effects become critically impor-

221

tant in close-up photography. There are two sources of artificial light of comparable energy: flash lamps in which the light is produced by chemical burning and electronic flash tubes in which the light is emitted by an excited gas. The former is a slow process permitting exposures at speeds within the limitations determined by the camera shutter. In the latter the exposure time is determined by the duration of the flash, which generally is about one-tenth of the maximum shutter speed. In both devices the flash is synchronized with the mechanical operation of the shutter. The advantage of electronic flash is in the shortness of the exposures it makes possible, allowing photography of small birds in rapid motion; its disadvantage is the weight of the apparatus needed to produce light of sufficient intensity.

To be suitable for bird photography a camera should meet certain fundamental requirements. The optimum image size is in the range from 2 x 2 to 4 x 5. For most purposes I prefer the largest. The camera should be well constructed and capable of considerable bellows extension for close-up focusing. For the sake of greater accuracy, it should be designed for ground-glass focusing either of the back or reflex type. Sheet film is preferable to roll film or film pack in the larger sizes, except when facilities for reloading holders are not available. The camera I generally use in conjunction with flash light is a 4 x 5 Graphic View equipped with a 7-inch Zeiss Protar lens, but I also use, as occasion demands, lenses of 6- to 9-inch focal lengths. Two very satisfactory lenses for a camera of this size are the 8-inch f/7.7 Commercial Ektar and the 9-inch

Goerz Artar. Fast lenses are neither necessary nor designed for close-up flash photography. The swing back of the view camera is a useful adjustment for obtaining maximum depth of focus.

Whichever method is used to provide an artificial source of light, the subject should be illuminated from more than one direction for the best modeling effects. Two lamps or flash tubes, and preferably three, can be arranged for pleasing lighting by placing one near the camera and the others to one side at 60 to 90 degrees from the camera axis. For greatest efficiency flash lamps must be used with reflectors. With black and white film overillumination of the subject is a danger. Two General Electric #11 lamps placed 30 inches from the subject will call for exposures at about f/32 and 1/200 second. However, because of the variables involved in all close-up photography of this sort, the initial exposure should be determined by actual trial to establish a basis for later calculation. It is also well to remember that the same numerical relationship holds between exposure and bellows extension, as well as between exposure and lamp-to-subject distance or aperture stop. With daylight color film, two General Electric #22B lamps must be used with a lens stop of about f/16.

The high speed of electronic flash allows the successful photography of birds regardless of their activity, whereas with flash lamps, even though synchronized at 1/200-second shutter speeds, sharp pictures can be obtained only when the birds are nearly motionless. My equipment consists of a 1000-watt-second power pack designed for operation from either a 110-volt a.c. line or a 6-volt storage battery. The energy of the pack is discharged through three sealed-beam tubes which are arranged, as described above, for side and fill-in lighting. They are supported on adjustable arms attached to the camera tripod. Whichever lighting system one uses, it is most convenient to operate it by electrical remote control from a point where the camera field can be clearly seen through binoculars. A blind is seldom necessary and is in fact an inconvenience if placed over the camera. For satisfactory results with color film the recommended correction filter must always be used.

With electronic flash it is possible to photograph birds as they are about to alight. Since the action is very fast, the shutter must be tripped at precisely the right moment during the time the bird is in the narrow field of the camera. It is very difficult to do this manually; the usual result is that the bird has either not entered the field or has already come to rest when the exposure is being made. This problem was solved by two British photographers, Eric Hosking and Cyril Newberry. As described in their book *Birds in Action*, they devised a photoelectric circuit that trips the shutter as the bird flies through a beam of light. However, the interruption of the beam at any point outside the camera field will also result in an exposure. To overcome this difficulty I have added a second beam which crosses the first at the point where I want to photograph the bird. Simultaneous interruption of both beams is required to trip the shutter, and the only place this can occur is where the beams cross.

Although most birds build their nests on or near the ground, one may often wish to photograph those that are beyond the range of a conventional tripod. For nests at moderate heights I carry on top of my car a large tripod made of two-by-fours which can be extended to eighteen feet. With it I use an extension ladder. For higher nests it is necessary either to build a platform in the tree or to erect a tower to support the equipment and, when needed, a blind.

Under certain conditions—when nests are very high in evergreens, for instance—it may be easier to bring the nests down to ground level than to raise the equipment to their height. This can be done by cutting off the branch on which the nest is built and lowering it gradually, allowing the adult birds time to become accustomed to each new position. One of the first that I moved in such a way was a nest of western tanagers in dense foliage almost forty feet above the ground and near the end of a long branch of a ponderosa pine overhanging a ravine. The branch curved upwards and, to prevent it from turning over after it was cut off, a strong wooden yoke was bolted to the top of the branch. To this a rope was attached, passed over a crotch higher in the tree, and made fast near the ground. Then the branch was sawed off and lowered about six feet. When the tanagers returned they were at first bewildered, and hovered around the place where the nest had formerly hung, but in a short time they became accustomed to the change. I thus managed to lower the branch to within two feet of the ground. After photographing, I hoisted the branch up again a few feet so that the young birds would not fall victim to predatory animals.

This drastic procedure should never be

used on a nest containing eggs, since it might lead to desertion of the nest, but the parental instinct in most birds is strong enough to prevent them from abandoning their young during such interference. Bird photographers have at times been severely criticized for the ruthlessness of their methods. Some of this criticism may be justified, but it should be pointed out that they are hardly less mindful of the welfare of the birds than bird painters who must at times shoot their specimens in order to paint them.

Even at its simplest, serious bird photography inevitably entails a great deal of work. Hours must be spent in the field finding the birds and their nests. Often the equipment is too bulky and heavy to be carried far by hand and a light automobile such as a jeep may be required.

Taking good bird pictures may seem, from what I have said, to require an extraordinary amount of effort. Whether such an expenditure of energy is worth while will depend on the results and on the satisfaction gained from the experience itself. My own attitude, and the best advice I can give to a beginner, is: never be satisfied, a better photograph is always possible.

Table of Photographs and Photographers

COLOR PLATES

PHOTOGRAPHS IN BLACK AND WHITE

Index of Birds

Numbers in italics refer to plate numbers of illustrations in color.

236

Acknowledgment and Credit

The Publisher wishes to thank the Photo Service Department of the National Audubon Society for help in assembling photographs.

Credit should also go to the following: Lucia Howe, for design; Chanticleer Company, New York, for color engraving; Empire Typographers, Inc., New York, for typesetting; Davis, Delaney, Inc., New York, for printing of color; Kipe Offset Process Co., New York, for printing of black and white pages; H. Wolff Book Manufacturing Co., New York, for binding.